THE AUSTRALIAN
Women's Weekly

monday to friday diet

keep weekends free for fun — an achievable way to lose weight

BAUER
MEDIA GROUP

CONTENTS

MEET THE DIETERS

It's true, we all want to lose weight at some stage of our lives, and it's harder for some than for others, which is why this weight-loss plan – diet during the week and eat what you like on the weekend – appealed to us. As the weight slowly came off, we found we didn't feel the need to overeat during our 'free' weekends. And we found the diet fitted into our work and home routines.

DAVID, our operations manager, is blessed with a girlfriend and mother who are both great cooks. Like most men, David loves his food, and tried hard to ignore his slowly increasing weight over the past couple of years. "I barely noticed a couple of extra kilos here and there," says David, "but it all eventually adds up to larger trousers." David found the diet easier than expected and lost 4.2kg.

FRAN, as food director of the Australian Women's Weekly, is constantly surrounded by food – all that testing and tasting is delicious, but eventually, as the saying goes, 'a minute on the lips is a lifetime on the hips'. Fran also felt the extra weight was making her tired and unfit. Testing the food on this diet helped Fran re-assess her lifestyle; she lost 6kg, and feels fitter, healthier and happier.

PAMELA is an old hand at dieting. As director of the Australian Women's Weekly Test Kitchen, Pamela, like Fran, tests and tastes all our recipes (not once, but three times for our triple-tested guarantee) and finds it hard to keep off the extra kilos. The fact that this diet allows more kilojoules than other diets, and has 'free' days, has helped Pamela maintain her weight loss of 3kg.

KERRY is our online editor and, as everyone who sits in front of a computer knows, unless you exercise regularly, this sedentary-style work is a fast way to download extra kilos. Kerry decided a pro-active approach was the way to go...take off the extra kilos before they became a problem. By sticking to the weekly menus, Kerry's status update is 3.2kg lost and a dress size down.

"This was a great diet for a bloke as the amount of food, more often than not, was really quite substantial — not feeling hungry all the time made it easy to stick to it. The big plus, however, was having weekends off.
– David

For me, the diet wasn't just about losing weight; it was also about feeling strong, vital and energised. And, the more I exercised, the more energy I gained. I find weight loss goes hand in hand with feeling better about yourself – being happier and more positive.
– Fran"

THE 5-DAY DIET

Want a healthy and sustainable diet that isn't a quick fix? One with a healthy eating plan that fits into your everyday routine? Well, the Monday-to-Friday diet is what you're searching for.

This diet will help you achieve and, most importantly, maintain your goal weight. This book provides you with a practical diet; the recipes are quick, filling and can easily be worked into anyone's busy lifestyle. The recipes, all of which serves two, are for breakfast, lunch and dinners for 20 mid-week days (four weeks). There are no recipes for you to follow on the weekend but, if you want to continue your good work, you could cook any of your favourites.

The recipes won't leave you feeling hungry; instead this diet offers you larger portion sizes and ensures you eat a wide variety of food from all five food groups, which include: fruit and vegetables (different types and colours); grain (cereal) foods, mostly wholegrain; reduced-fat dairy products; lean meats and poultry, fish, eggs, tofu, nuts, seeds and legumes. Eating a diet containing a variety from each of these food groups helps to maintain a healthy weight and fight off the risk of chronic illness. For more information on what to place on your plate go to: www.eatforhealth.gov.au

Following a healthy, but realistic, diet is integral if you want to improve your overall health and wellbeing. This diet ensures you only consume a maximum of 6200kJ (1500 calories) per day, including snacks. By the time the four weeks have passed, you will be feeling fitter, healthier and happier.

THE ROAD TO SUCCESS
Exercise

While a healthy diet is an important factor for losing weight, it means nothing without engaging in some form of regular exercise. There are lots of ways to squeeze exercise into your day. Wake up a little earlier and go for a 30-minute walk around the block or, if you can, walk to work. Take your exercise clothes to work and walk during your lunch break; alternatively, swap that coffee with a friend to a walk instead – making your exercise social will encourage you to get out and about. Regular exercise will help build up muscle, an ideal result, as muscle burns more energy than fatty tissue.

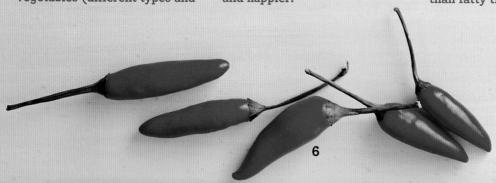

Don't forget to drink lots of water to keep your body hydrated. We suggest drinking at least two litres of water every day.

Motivation

Before starting the diet make sure you are 100% committed. Your commitment and drive is the only thing that can help you break bad habits. Unlike other diets, don't expect the weight to shift overnight – this diet will take a little longer as it is all about ensuring you can implement the diet into your lifestyle and maintain your weight loss.

To keep you motivated you might find it easier to set a goal – perhaps you want to tone your tummy, or zip-up your jeans without having to do the 'jean dance'. Write your goal down, in your phone or on paper, but make sure it is clearly visible at all times. Every time you look at it, it'll give you motivation to keep going and achieve your goal. This is especially important on those days when you're feeling down and are really tempted to grab an unhealthy snack or meal. Seeing your goal will give you incentive to keep on track.

Get organised

When following any diet, it is paramount you get organised early. With busy lifestyles, it is easy to arrive home too tired to cook, and instead choose fattier takeaway options. Plan ahead. Do all your grocery shopping on the weekend so you don't give into that greasy pizza temptation. It is so easy to find a quick alternative to takeaway if you have fresh fruit and vegetables in the fridge.

Don't undo all your good work on the weekend

When it comes to the weekend don't forget everything you learned during the week. The weekend allows you to let your hair down and eat whatever you like, but remember, you will attain your goal sooner if you keep everything in moderation.

Opt for healthy choices, such as fresh foods, and stay away from overly-processed foods. When eating out, ask for the dressing on the side, avoid fatty foods and, when possible, avoid over-indulging in alcohol and soft drinks.

SHOPPING LIST

FRIDGE

- 250g block butter
- 120g reduced-fat fetta
- 140g reduced-fat ricotta
- 1 small block parmesan
- 8 eggs
- 1 litre skim milk
- 600ml buttermilk
- 1 small packet frozen peas
- 250g firm tofu
- 500g low-fat plain yoghurt
- 280g low-fat vanilla yoghurt
- 40g black olives

FRUIT

- 1 small apple
- 3 fresh apricots
- 1 small banana
- 5 medium lemons
- 3 limes
- 1 large mango
- 1 medium pear
- ¼ small pineapple
- 3 plums
- 250g raspberries
- 1 bunch rhubarb
- 400g rockmelon
- 150g strawberries
- 1 medium white peach
- 1 medium yellow nectarine

VEGETABLES

- 170g asparagus
- 1 small avocado
- 2 baby buk choy
- 200g green beans
- 1 small red capsicum
- 2 large carrots
- ½ small cauliflower
- 1 stalk celery
- 1 fresh long green chilli
- 2 fresh long red chillies
- 1 lebanese cucumber
- 10 cloves garlic
- 20g piece fresh ginger
- 1 butter lettuce
- 1 cos lettuce
- 1 small iceberg lettuce
- 200g button mushrooms
- 2 small brown onions
- 5 green onions
- 2 small red onions
- 150g snow peas
- 60g baby spinach leaves
- 80g cherry tomatoes
- 250g grape tomatoes

HERBS

- 1 bunch basil
- 1 bunch chives
- 1 bunch coriander
- 1 bunch dill
- 1 bunch flat-leaf parsley
- 2 bunches mint
- 1 bunch oregano

MEAT

- 2 x 150g eye-fillet beef steaks
- ½ barbecued chicken
- 180g minced chicken
- 120g sliced light ham
- 2 slices prosciutto
- 2 x 100g lamb backstraps
- 140g thin slices turkey

SEAFOOD

- 2 x 150g skinless white fish fillets
- 60g thin slices smoked salmon
- 1kg black mussels

WEEK 1

Yes, starting a diet is hard, and the first week can either make or break your dieting willpower, but this one has more kilojoules than most diets, so it shouldn't be as painful as you think. It's important to be in the right frame of mind when starting a diet, otherwise you'll have failed before you've begun.

diary entry

Kicked off the proceedings with a weigh-in at home where I tried really hard to ignore my starting weight. The greek omelette for breakfast was delicious and surprisingly substantial – it was a great way to start the diet.
– David

Breakfast this morning could have been from my favourite café. I loved every bite, which I've never been able to say about diet food before.
– Kerry

greek omelette

PREP + COOK TIME 15 MINUTES **SERVES** 2

cooking-oil spray

60g (2 ounces) baby spinach leaves

80g (2½ ounces) cherry tomatoes, halved

1 clove garlic, crushed

6 egg whites

1 tablespoon coarsely chopped fresh dill

2 tablespoons skim milk

40g (1½ ounces) reduced-fat fetta, crumbled

2 tablespoons halved black olives

2 slices dark rye bread (90g), toasted

2 lemon wedges

1 Lightly spray a small non-stick frying pan with oil. Cook spinach, tomato and garlic, stirring, over medium heat, for 2 minutes or until spinach is just wilted. Remove from pan.

2 Whisk egg whites, dill and milk in a small bowl.

3 Lightly spray the same pan. Pour in half the egg-white mixture; cook, over medium heat, for 2 minutes or until just set. Top with half the fetta, half the olives and half the spinach mixture. Fold over to enclose. Remove from pan and keep warm (see tips).

4 Repeat step 3 to make a second omelette. Serve the omelettes with toast and lemon; sprinkle with extra dill, if you like.

nutritional count per serving
- ▶ 8.2g total fat
- ▶ 2.6g saturated fat
- ▶ 1237kJ (295 cal)
- ▶ 23.3g carbohydrate
- ▶ 29g protein
- ▶ 5.2g fibre

test kitchen tips

Keep the first omelette warm in a slow oven while you cook the second one. For a fluffy omelette, whisk the egg whites until soft peaks form.

spicy ham and avocado wrap

PREP TIME 10 MINUTES **SERVES** 2

½ **small avocado (100g), sliced thinly lengthways**

¼ **teaspoon each smoked paprika and ground cumin**

1 **teaspoon lime juice**

2 x 20cm (8-inch) **wholegrain tortillas**

6 **thin slices light ham (60g)**

100g (3 ounces) **drained char-grilled capsicum (bell pepper)**

60g (2 ounces) **butter (boston) lettuce leaves**

2 **tablespoons spicy tomato salsa**

1 Combine avocado, spices and juice in a small bowl. Arrange over tortillas.
2 Top tortillas with ham, capsicum, lettuce and salsa. Roll to enclose filling.

tips You could also use mountain bread or lavash. This is a good work lunch; you can store the ingredients in separate containers and assemble the wrap just before serving.

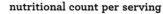

nutritional count per serving
▶ 13.6g total fat
▶ 2.6g saturated fat
▶ 1053kJ (251 cal)
▶ 19.5g carbohydrate
▶ 10.3g protein
▶ 5.4g fibre

diary entry

The ham wrap for lunch was tasty, but I could have eaten another one. Being a constant snacker, I was pretty hungry by 5pm, and I felt my energy level drop considerably in the afternoon.– David

nutritional count per serving
▶ 9.4g total fat
▶ 2.6g saturated fat
▶ 1420kJ (339 cal)
▶ 31g carbohydrate
▶ 27g protein
▶ 10.6g fibre

tomato and carrot soup with chicken meatballs

PREP + COOK TIME 35 MINUTES SERVES 2

cooking-oil spray

1 small brown onion (80g), chopped finely

2 large carrots (360g), chopped coarsely

2 cloves garlic, crushed

400g (12½ ounces) canned diced tomatoes

2 cups (500ml) salt-reduced chicken stock

180g (5½ ounces) minced (ground) chicken

1 tablespoon finely chopped fresh basil

1 egg white

⅓ cup (25g) stale breadcrumbs

1 tablespoon low-fat plain yoghurt

1 lime

1 tablespoon fresh baby basil leaves, extra

2 slices multigrain bread (90g), toasted

1 Lightly spray a medium saucepan with oil; cook onion, carrot and half the garlic, over medium heat, for 5 minutes or until onion is tender.

2 Add tomatoes and stock; bring to the boil. Reduce to a simmer; cook soup for 20 minutes or until carrots are tender. Remove from heat; stand for 10 minutes, then blend or process until almost smooth. Season to taste.

3 Meanwhile, combine chicken, basil, remaining garlic, egg white and breadcrumbs in a medium bowl. Roll 2 level teaspoons of the mince mixture into balls. Heat a lightly oiled non-stick frying pan; cook meatballs, over medium heat, for 8 minutes or until browned all over and cooked through.

4 Return soup to pan, add meatballs; cook, over low heat, until heated through. Top soup with yoghurt and a squeeze of lime; sprinkle with extra basil leaves. Serve with toast.

tips Try adding other herbs to the meatballs such as oregano, thyme or sage. Uncooked meatballs can be frozen for up to three months. Wrap in plastic and place in an airtight container. If you like, serve soup with a slice of toasted wholegrain bread, rather than the multigrain.

quinoa porridge with vanilla stewed rhubarb

PREP + COOK TIME 15 MINUTES SERVES 2

| 3 stalks rhubarb (185g), chopped into 3cm (1¼-inch) lengths |
| ½ teaspoon vanilla extract |
| 1 teaspoon honey |
| 2 teaspoons water |
| 1 cup (60g) quinoa flakes |
| 2 cups (500ml) skim milk |
| 1½ tablespoons honey, extra |

1 Combine rhubarb, vanilla, honey and the water in a microwave-safe bowl; cover with kitchen paper. Microwave mixture on HIGH (100%) for 3 minutes or until tender.
2 Combine quinoa and milk in a medium saucepan; cook, stirring, over medium-high heat, for about 4 minutes or until porridge thickens.
3 Top porridge with rhubarb and extra honey.

tips Quinoa flakes are available in the health food aisle of the supermarket or from health food stores. You could use rolled oats, if you prefer. The rhubarb can be cooked in a small covered saucepan over medium heat for about 10 minutes or until tender.

nutritional count per serving
▶ 2.3g total fat
▶ 0.6g saturated fat
▶ 1274kJ (304 cal)
▶ 53g carbohydrate
▶ 16.2g protein
▶ 4.2g fibre

turkey caesar salad sandwich

PREP + COOK TIME 10 MINUTES SERVES 2

2 thin slices prosciutto (30g), halved

4 thin slices dark rye bread (180g), toasted

¼ cup (75g) low-fat dijonnaise

6 thin slices turkey (140g)

4 cos (romaine) lettuce leaves

¼ cup flaked parmesan (20g)

1 Preheat grill (broiler). Place prosciutto on a baking tray; grill for 1 minute or until crisp.
2 Spread two pieces of toast with dijonnaise; top with turkey, lettuce, parmesan and prosciutto then remaining toast slices.

tip If you can't find low-fat dijonnaise, you can use 2 tablespoons low-fat mayonnaise combined with 1 teaspoon wholegrain mustard.

diary entry

My energy levels seemed to drop further today. I was hungry and had a headache and think these are most likely withdrawal symptoms from all the not-so-healthy food I am used to eating. Guess this means the diet is working. – David

Breakfast was a great start – while I prefer quinoa in a salad, it made a nice change to oats in the porridge. This was a generous serve that kept me satisfied until lunch. – Fran

nutritional count per serving

▶ 11g total fat   ▶ 46.1g carbohydrate

▶ 3.9g saturated fat   ▶ 37.1g protein

▶ 1871kJ (447 cal)   ▶ 6.4g fibre

roasted lamb with tagine sauce

PREP + COOK TIME 40 MINUTES SERVES 2

½ small cauliflower (500g), cut into large florets

cooking-oil spray

2 x 100g (3-ounce) lamb backstraps

1 teaspoon ground cumin

200g (6½ ounces) green beans, trimmed

1 small brown onion (80g), chopped finely

1 clove garlic, crushed

½ teaspoon ground cinnamon

2 teaspoons ground cumin, extra

400g (12½ ounces) canned diced tomatoes

2 tablespoons currants

¼ cup (60ml) water

1 teaspoon salt-reduced chicken stock powder

2 teaspoons honey

¼ cup (70g) low-fat plain yoghurt

¼ cup fresh mint leaves

1 Preheat oven to 180°C/350°F.

2 Line an oven tray with baking paper. Place the cauliflower on the tray, lightly spray with oil; roast for 15 minutes.

3 Meanwhile, sprinkle lamb with cumin. Lightly spray lamb and beans with oil; add to cauliflower. Roast for 10 minutes or until vegetables are tender and lamb is cooked to your liking. Stand covered to keep warm.

4 Meanwhile, lightly spray a medium frying pan with oil; cook onion, garlic, cinnamon and extra cumin, stirring occasionally, over medium heat, for 5 minutes or until onion is softened. Add tomato, currants, the water, stock and honey, bring to the boil; reduce heat, simmer for 5 minutes or until sauce thickens slightly. Remove from heat; season to taste.

5 Slice lamb; serve with roasted vegetables and tagine sauce. Top with yoghurt and mint.

nutritional count per serving
- 8.2g total fat
- 2.6g saturated fat
- 1401kJ (335 cal)
- 35.3g carbohydrate
- 22.6g protein
- 13.9g fibre

mango and almond smoothie

PREP TIME 5 MINUTES **SERVES** 2

1 large mango (600g), chopped coarsely

¼ cup (30g) ground almonds

1 cup (250ml) skim milk

½ cup (140g) low-fat plain yoghurt

1 teaspoon vanilla extract

1 tablespoon lime juice

1 tablespoon honey

ice cubes, to serve

1 Blend or process mango, ground almonds, milk, yoghurt, vanilla, juice and half the honey until smooth.

2 Place ice into tall glasses; pour mango mixture over ice. Drizzle with remaining honey and sprinkle with grated lime rind, if you like.

tip Use frozen mango or drained canned mango in natural juice, if fresh is unavailable. Blend or process the ice cubes with the ingredients for a thicker smoothie.

nutritional count per serving
▶ 14.4g total fat
▶ 4.2g saturated fat
▶ 1924kJ (460 cal)
▶ 64.2g carbohydrate
▶ 15.6g protein
▶ 4.7g fibre

nutritional count per serving

▶ 10.6g total fat   ▶ 32g carbohydrate
▶ 1.6g saturated fat   ▶ 15.3g protein
▶ 1222kJ (292 cal)   ▶ 5.9g fibre

sushi-style smoked salmon salad

PREP + COOK TIME 20 MINUTES **SERVES** 2

250g (8-ounce) packet microwave brown rice

2 teaspoons rice wine vinegar

1 teaspoon caster (superfine) sugar

150g (4½ ounces) snow peas, halved diagonally

1 green onion (scallion), halved crossways

1 lebanese cucumber (130g), sliced thinly lengthways (see tips)

4 thin slices smoked salmon (60g)

¼ small avocado (50g), sliced thinly lengthways

1 sheet nori (seaweed), cut into diamonds

1 teaspoon each white and black sesame seeds, toasted

1½ tablespoons tamari

1½ tablespoons water

½ teaspoon wasabi paste

1 tablespoon pickled ginger

1 Cook rice according to directions on packet. Combine rice with vinegar and sugar in a large bowl. Stand until cool.

2 Place snow peas in a small heatproof bowl; cover with boiling water, stand for 1 minute, drain. Rinse under cold water; drain.

3 Thinly slice white part of the onion diagonally. Thinly slice green part lengthways; place in a bowl of iced water to curl. Combine snow peas, cucumber, salmon, avocado and white part of onion in a bowl.

4 Serve rice with salad; sprinkle with nori, sesame seeds and green onion. Combine tamari, the water and wasabi in a screw-top jar, shake well; drizzle over salad. Top with ginger, and extra wasabi, if you like.

tips Use a vegetable peeler to cut the cucumber into ribbons. If taking the salad to work for lunch, keep the dressing separate until ready to serve.

test kitchen tips

You can use other asian greens such as choy sum, instead of the buk choy. The asian pesto can be made a day ahead; cover tightly with plastic wrap and store in the fridge.

char-grilled steak with asian pesto

PREP + COOK TIME 25 MINUTES **SERVES** 2

2 x 150g (4½-ounce) beef eye-fillet steaks

1 teaspoon cracked black pepper

cooking-oil spray

90g (3 ounces) soba noodles

2 baby buk choy (300g), halved lengthways

ASIAN PESTO

2 cups firmly packed fresh coriander leaves (cilantro)

1 cup firmly packed fresh mint leaves

1 green onion (scallion), chopped coarsely

1 fresh long green chilli, chopped coarsely

1 clove garlic, crushed

3 teaspoons light soy sauce

1 tablespoon lime juice

¼ cup (60ml) water

1 teaspoon sesame oil

1 Make asian pesto.

2 Sprinkle beef with pepper. Lightly spray a heated grill plate (or grill or barbecue) with oil; cook beef for 4 minutes each side, or until cooked as desired. Cover; rest for 5 minutes.

3 Meanwhile, cook noodles in a large saucepan of boiling water for about 2 minutes. Add buk choy; cook a further 2 minutes or until buk choy and noodles are tender; drain.

4 Serve beef with noodles, buk choy and pesto.

asian pesto Blend or process ingredients until well combined.

---

nutritional count per serving

▶ 12.3g total fat ▶ 15g carbohydrate

▶ 3.9g saturated fat ▶ 45.9g protein

▶ 1586kJ (379 cal) ▶ 12g fibre

" diary entry

I've never been much of a smoothie or juice kind of girl, but I did enjoy the mango smoothie breakfast and it was delicious and filling. Lunch packed a real punch with great flavours. Dinner was also filling and I loved it. So far I'm not craving chocolate or sweets after dinner.
– Fran

Breakfast was a delight, although I did get hungry around 11am. I snacked on a banana, instead of a biscuit, which helped me through to the very tasty lunch. Thank goodness dinner was filling, and I was able to resist the chocolate my unhelpful husband brought home."
– Kerry

stone fruit with strawberry rosewater swirl yoghurt

PREP TIME 10 MINUTES **SERVES** 2

1 medium white peach (150g), sliced thinly

1 medium yellow nectarine (170g), sliced thinly

1 plum (110g), sliced thinly

1 apricot (75g), sliced thinly

2 tablespoons coarsely chopped pistachios

STRAWBERRY ROSEWATER SWIRL YOGHURT

150g (4½ ounces) strawberries, sliced

1 tablespoon rosewater

1 cup (280g) low-fat vanilla yoghurt

1 Make strawberry rosewater yoghurt.

2 Divide peach, nectarine, plum and apricot between two bowls.

3 Spoon strawberry rosewater yoghurt over fruit; sprinkle with nuts.

strawberry rosewater swirl yoghurt Blend or process strawberries with rosewater until smooth. Swirl through yoghurt.

nutritional count per serve
▶ 6.8g total fat
▶ 1.1g saturated fat
▶ 1223kJ (292 cal)
▶ 38.7g carbohydrate
▶ 13.4g protein
▶ 6.7g fibre

test kitchen tips

You can use thawed frozen
strawberries or raspberries
for this recipe. Either white or
yellow peaches and nectarines
can be used in this recipe.

chicken, walnut and fetta pasta salad

PREP + COOK TIME 25 MINUTES **SERVES** 2

100g (3 ounces) wholemeal penne

1 cup (160g) coarsely shredded cooked chicken

1 cup loosely packed fresh flat-leaf parsley leaves

¼ cup (25g) coarsely chopped walnuts, toasted

80g (2½ ounces) reduced-fat fetta, crumbled

1 trimmed stalk celery (100g), sliced finely

1 small apple (130g), sliced finely

½ small red onion (50g), sliced finely

¼ cup (60ml) 99% fat-free vinaigrette

1 Cook pasta in a large saucepan of boiling water until just tender. Drain, rinse under cold water, drain.

2 Combine pasta with remaining ingredients in a large bowl; toss gently.

tips Use barbecued chicken breast with the skin removed, leftover roast chicken, or pan-fried or poached chicken breasts. If making ahead of time, don't dress the salad until ready to serve. We used a fat-free french vinaigrette, but dress the salad with your favourite fat-free dressing.

diary entry

I loved breakfast – fruit, nuts and yoghurt. I'm feeling good, better than during the other three days, and feel like I've broken the 'I'm on a diet' barrier.
– Pamela

nutritional count per serving

▶ 17.5g total fat ▶ 41.2g carbohydrate

▶ 5g saturated fat ▶ 45.1g protein

▶ 2516kJ (529 cal) ▶ 11.5g fibre

nutritional count per serving
▶ 4.6g total fat
▶ 1.4g saturated fat
▶ 1446kJ (345 cal)
▶ 23.3g carbohydrate
▶ 46.1g protein
▶ 17.2g fibre

pan-fried fish with green purée

PREP + COOK TIME 20 MINUTES **SERVES** 2

cooking-oil spray

2 x 150g (4½-ounce) skinless white fish fillets

170g (5½ ounces) asparagus, trimmed

1½ cups (180g) frozen peas

400g (12½ ounces) canned cannellini beans, rinsed, drained

1 clove garlic, crushed

2 tablespoons shredded fresh flat-leaf parsley

2 teaspoons coarsely grated lemon rind

1 clove garlic, extra, sliced thinly

1 medium lemon (140g)

1 Lightly spray a large non-stick frying pan with oil; cook fish and asparagus, over medium heat, for 3 minutes each side or until fish is cooked through.
2 Place peas in a medium heatproof bowl; cover with boiling water for 1 minute, drain. Blend or process peas, beans and garlic until smooth.
3 Place bean purée in a microwave-safe bowl, cover; cook on MEDIUM HIGH (75%) for 1 minute or until warmed through.
4 Combine parsley, rind and extra garlic in a small bowl.
5 Top purée with fish and asparagus; sprinkle with parsley mixture and serve with a squeeze of lemon.

serving suggestion Serve with green beans instead of the asparagus, if you like.

tip We used wahoo fish for this recipe, but you could use any white fish such as whiting, bream, sole, flounder, dory, perch, snapper or ling.

25

test kitchen tips

One muffin is to be served per person for breakfast. The remaining muffins can be frozen or eaten as a snack. You could make two large muffins for breakfast and the remaining mixture can be made into snack-sized mini muffins. The ricotta mixture serves 2 people; make a fresh batch before serving the remaining muffins. Freeze the extra muffins in a ziptop bag or an airtight container for up to 3 months. Thaw at room temperature.

diary entry

The muffin for breakfast felt like a treat. Strangely, at 1pm I still wasn't hungry. While I loved the mussels for dinner, the fact it was Friday meant I felt I was missing out on all the usual Friday night food, but I was proud of myself for sticking to the diet all week. – David

Breakfast was delicious, but I was hungry by 10:30am. And, while lunch was tasty, it didn't hit the spot either. I resisted snacks all afternoon, and by dinner I was starving. The mussels were delicious, but 2 hours later I was hungry again. I caved in and ate a piece of toast. – Kerry

savoury breakfast muffin with chive ricotta

PREP + COOK TIME 35 MINUTES **MAKES** 6 MUFFINS

1 cup (160g) wholemeal plain (all-purpose) flour

½ cup (75g) plain (all-purpose) flour

2 teaspoons baking powder

¼ teaspoon bicarbonate of soda (baking soda)

2 green onions (scallions), sliced thinly

60g (2 ounces) reduced-fat sliced ham, chopped coarsely

50g (1½ ounces) drained char-grilled capsicum (bell pepper), chopped coarsely

1 tablespoon coarsely chopped fresh chives

1 egg

1 cup (250ml) buttermilk

1½ tablespoons vegetable oil

¼ cup (70g) dijon mustard

CHIVE RICOTTA

½ cup (120g) low-fat ricotta

1 tablespoon finely chopped fresh chives

2 teaspoons lemon juice

1 Preheat oven to 180°C/350°F. Line six holes of a ¾-cup (180ml) texas muffin pan with large muffin paper cases.

2 Combine sifted flours, baking powder and soda in a large bowl. Stir in onion, ham, capsicum and chives.

3 Whisk egg, buttermilk, oil and mustard in a small jug. Pour egg mixture into dry ingredients; stir until just combined. Spoon mixture evenly into pans. Bake for about 25 minutes. Stand muffins in pan for 5 minutes before turning, top-side up, onto a wire rack to cool.

4 Meanwhile, make chive ricotta; serve with muffins.

chive ricotta Combine ingredients in a small bowl.

nutritional count per serving
(1 serving consists of one muffin and
half the ricotta mixture)
▶ 9.8g total fat   ▶ 23.3g carbohydrate
▶ 3.5g saturated fat   ▶ 14.8g protein
▶ 1032kJ (247 cal)   ▶ 3.2g fibre

vegetarian sang choy bow

PREP + COOK TIME 25 MINUTES **SERVES** 2

cooking-oil spray

1 clove garlic, crushed

4cm (1½-inch) piece fresh ginger (20g), grated

1 fresh long red chilli, sliced thinly

200g (6½ ounces) button mushrooms, chopped finely

¾ cup (150g) sliced canned water chestnuts

250g (8 ounces) firm tofu, chopped finely

¼ cup (60ml) sweet chilli sauce

3 teaspoons light soy sauce

4 iceberg lettuce leaves, trimmed

1 green onion (scallion), sliced thinly

2 tablespoons fresh coriander leaves (cilantro)

2 tablespoons fresh mint leaves

1 lime

1 Lightly spray a heated large non-stick frying pan with oil; cook garlic, ginger, chilli, mushrooms, water chestnuts and tofu over high heat, stirring, for 10 minutes or until browned.

2 Add sauces to pan; cook for 30 seconds. Spoon mixture into lettuce leaves; top with onion, coriander and mint. Serve with a squeeze of lime juice. Sprinkle with extra chilli, if you like.

tips For a non-vegetarian option, substitute tofu with lean chicken mince. You could use butter (boston) lettuce leaves, if you like. For a hint of heat, add 1 finely chopped red thai (serrano) chilli.

tomato chilli mussels

PREP + COOK TIME 25 MINUTES **SERVES** 2

cooking-oil spray

2 cloves garlic, sliced

1 small red onion (100g), sliced thinly

1 small red capsicum (bell pepper) (150g), sliced thinly

4 sprigs fresh oregano

400g (12½ ounces) canned diced tomatoes

1kg (2 pounds) black mussels, cleaned

420g (13½ ounces) canned chickpeas (garbanzo beans), rinsed, drained

¼ cup loosely packed fresh flat-leaf parsley leaves

1 fresh long red chilli, sliced thinly

1 medium lemon (140g)

1 Lightly spray a heated large saucepan with oil; cook garlic for 1 minute or until golden. Remove from pan. Add onion, capsicum and oregano to pan; cook, stirring, over medium heat, for 5 minutes or until onion is tender.
2 Add tomatoes, mussels and chickpeas to pan; cook, covered, for 8 minutes or until mussels open.
3 Sprinkle with garlic, parsley and chilli. Serve with a squeeze of lemon.

tips If you prefer, buy 1kg (2-pound) packs of pot-ready mussels from fishmongers or seafood markets. These have already been scrubbed and bearded, and are ready to cook. Some mussels might not open. These might need prompting with a knife or might not have cooked as quickly as the others – some will not open after excessive cooking. You do not have to discard these, just open with a knife and cook a little more if you wish.

nutritional count per serving
▶ 7.3g total fat
▶ 1.6g saturated fat
▶ 1603kJ (383 cal)
▶ 38.4g carbohydrate
▶ 34.1g protein
▶ 14.4g fibre

SHOPPING LIST

FRIDGE

- 1 tub extra-light spreadable cream cheese
- 1 small block parmesan
- 140g reduced-fat ricotta
- 9 eggs
- 1 litre skim milk
- 1 small carton light sour cream
- 500g low-fat plain yoghurt
- 200g low-fat vanilla yoghurt
- 1 packet frozen edamame peas

FRUIT

- 1 punnet blackberries
- 1 punnet blueberries
- 2 figs
- 8 medium lemons
- 3 limes
- 1 medium mandarin
- 1 small mango
- 2 small ruby (pink) grapefruit
- 4 medium oranges
- 2 small pears
- 1 punnet raspberries
- 2 x 250g punnets strawberries
- ½ small watermelon

VEGETABLES

- 1 small avocado
- 150g green beans
- 1 small red capsicum
- 2 small carrots
- 1 bunch cavolo nero
- 4 sticks celery
- 1 corn cob
- 2 lebanese cucumbers
- 1 small eggplant
- 9 cloves garlic
- 10g piece ginger
- 2 small kumara
- 1 baby cos lettuce
- 120g mesclun salad leaves
- 1 small brown onion
- 3 green onions
- 1 medium red onion
- 3 small red onions
- 5 medium tomatoes
- 250g mixed medley tomatoes
- 1 bunch rocket
- 400g butternut pumpkin
- 500g jap pumpkin

HERBS

- 1 bunch basil
- 1 bunch chives
- 1 bunch coriander
- 1 bunch dill
- 1 bunch flat-leaf parsley
- 2 bunches mint
- 1 bunch oregano

MEAT

- 80g low-fat shortcut bacon rashers
- 4 x 50g beef minute steaks
- 80g sliced rare roast beef
- 1 barbecued chicken
- 350g lean minced lamb
- 200g minced turkey

SEAFOOD

- 500g uncooked small king prawns

WEEK 2

Our dieters found they didn't over-indulge as much as they thought they would during the first 'free' weekend. And, although David certainly enjoyed his usual fare at the football, he didn't eat as many of the high-kilojoule, high-fat offerings as usual. Every meat pie and chocolate relinquished, comes off the hips!

gingerbread-spiced fig muesli

PREP + COOK TIME 20 MINUTES **MAKES** 6 CUPS

1⅓ cups (145g) rolled rye

1⅓ cups (80g) wheat bran flakes

1⅓ cups (120g) rolled oats

⅓ cup (65g) pepitas (pumpkin seeds)

⅓ cup (35g) walnuts, toasted

1 cup (190g) dried figs, halved

1 cup (150g) raisins

1 teaspoon mixed spice

2 teaspoons ground ginger

1 cup (250ml) skim milk

2 fresh figs (120g), quartered

1 Preheat oven to 180°C/350°F.

2 Place rolled rye on a baking tray. Bake for 10 minutes or until crisp; cool.

3 Combine rolled rye, wheat bran flakes, rolled oats, pepitas, walnuts, dried figs, raisins, mixed spice and ginger in a large bowl.

4 To serve, place ¾ cup muesli in each bowl; top each with ½ cup milk and fresh figs.

tip Replace fresh figs with stone fruit or berries.

nutritional count per serving

▶ 9.1g total fat
▶ 1.3g saturated fat
▶ 1687kJ (403 cal)
▶ 61.8g carbohydrate
▶ 12.4g protein
▶ 10.5g fibre

diary entry

Week 2, and I've learned that if I eat healthy most of the time, I don't feel so guilty when I occasionally indulge. I didn't overeat during the weekend, and feel happier for it. Today's food was delicious and satisfying. I'm eating more now than before the diet, but I'm not eating chocolate. – Fran

Left to my own devices (or should that be vices?) over the weekend, and I didn't behave too badly. The first weigh-in after a week revealed that I've lost 1.7kg – I'm happy with that, it's a good start. – Pamela

test kitchen tips

You can buy rolled rye at health food stores; replace it with rolled oats if you can't find it. Store the muesli in an airtight container in the fridge for up to 3 months.

sticky pomegranate koftas with herb couscous

PREP + COOK TIME 30 MINUTES **SERVES** 2

200g (6½ ounces) lean minced (ground) lamb

1 teaspoon garam masala

1 clove garlic, crushed

cooking-oil spray

1 tablespoon pomegranate molasses

⅓ cup (95g) low-fat plain yoghurt

HERB COUSCOUS

½ cup (100g) wholemeal couscous

½ cup (125ml) boiling water

½ cup loosely packed fresh mint leaves

½ cup loosely packed fresh flat-leaf parsley leaves

150g (4½ ounces) mixed medley tomatoes, halved

80g (2½ ounces) drained char-grilled capsicum (bell pepper), sliced thinly

1 tablespoon lemon juice

1 Combine lamb, garam masala and garlic in a medium bowl. Season; roll lamb into 10 even ovals. Lightly spray a heated large non-stick frying pan with oil; cook kofta, over medium heat, turning occasionally, for 8 minutes or until cooked through. Add pomegranate molasses; cook for 30 seconds.
2 Meanwhile, make herb couscous. Serve koftas with couscous; drizzle with yoghurt. Sprinkle with lemon rind, if you like.

herb couscous Combine couscous and the water in a large heatproof bowl, cover; stand for 5 minutes or until liquid is absorbed, fluffing with a fork occasionally. Stir in mint, parsley, tomato, capsicum and juice. Season to taste.

tips Pomegranate molasses is made from reduced pomegranate juice, lemon juice and sugar. It has a sweet yet tart flavour. You can buy it from select larger supermarkets and specialty food stores. Kofta can be prepared 2 days ahead; store, covered, in the fridge. Uncooked kofta can be frozen in an airtight container for up to 3 months.

nutritional count per serving
▶ 15.4g total fat
▶ 5.2g saturated fat
▶ 1998kJ (477 cal)
▶ 43.2g carbohydrate
▶ 37.7g protein
▶ 11.1g fibre

harissa beef with garlic beans and pumpkin mash

PREP + COOK TIME 35 MINUTES **SERVES** 2

4 x 50g (1½-ounce) beef minute steaks

1 tablespoon lemon juice

1 tablespoon harissa paste (see tips)

400g (12½ ounces) butternut pumpkin, chopped coarsely

1 tablespoon low-fat plain yoghurt

cooking-oil spray

1 bunch cavolo nero (tuscan cabbage) (125g), chopped coarsely

150g (4½ ounces) green beans, trimmed

1 Combine steak, juice and half the harissa in a large bowl; toss to coat.

2 Boil, steam or microwave pumpkin until tender; mash until smooth. Stir in yoghurt; season to taste. Cover to keep warm.

3 Lightly spray a heated grill pan (or grill or barbecue) with oil; cook steaks, over high heat, for 1 minute each side or until cooked as desired. Remove from pan; cover to keep warm.

4 Cook cavolo nero in the same heated pan, stirring occasionally, for 2 minutes or until wilted, season to taste.

5 Cook beans in a saucepan of boiling water for 2 minutes or until tender. Drain.

6 Serve steaks with mash, cavolo nero and beans. Dollop with remaining harissa. Accompany with lemon wedges, if you like.

nutritional count per serving
▶ 10.7g total fat
▶ 3.2g saturated fat
▶ 1464kJ (350 cal)
▶ 27.6g carbohydrate
▶ 0.8g protein
▶ 9.8g fibre

test kitchen tips

If you don't like very spicy
food, replace 2 teaspoons of
the harissa paste with water.
Substitute cavolo nero with
cabbage or silver beet.

breakfast mezze for two

PREP + COOK TIME 20 MINUTES SERVES 2

1 wholemeal pitta bread (70g)

cooking-oil spray

2 teaspoons za'atar

2 x 50g (1½ ounce) soft-boiled eggs, peeled

½ small avocado (100g), sliced thickly

1 medium tomato (150g), sliced thickly

⅓ cup (80g) reduced-fat ricotta

¼ teaspoon chilli flakes

80g (2½ ounces) rocket (arugula) leaves

2 lemon wedges

1 Preheat grill (broiler). Lightly spray pitta bread with oil; sprinkle with za'atar. Cook under hot grill for 2 minutes or until crisp. Break into coarse pieces.
2 Place remaining ingredients on a serving platter; sprinkle ricotta with chilli; serve with pitta pieces.

tips To make the perfect soft-boiled eggs, place eggs in a small saucepan and barely cover with cold water. Cover the pan and bring to the boil; then boil, uncovered, for 3 minutes, drain. Shell eggs when cool enough to handle. You can use either heirloom or cherry tomatoes, if you like.

nutritional count per serving
- ▶ 16.7g total fat
- ▶ 5g saturated fat
- ▶ 1285kJ (307 cal)
- ▶ 21.2g carbohydrate
- ▶ 15.5g protein
- ▶ 5.5g fibre

chicken and watermelon rice noodle salad

PREP TIME 20 MINUTES SERVES 2

100g (3 ounces) rice vermicelli

1¼ cups shredded cooked chicken (200g)

1 small carrot (70g), cut into matchsticks

2 green onions (scallions), sliced thinly lengthways

1 lebanese cucumber (130g), cut into matchsticks

250g (8 ounces) watermelon, cut into thin wedges

¼ cup loosely packed fresh coriander leaves (cilantro)

¼ cup loosely packed fresh mint leaves

¼ cup (70g) plum sauce

1 tablespoon light soy sauce

2 tablespoons water

2cm (¾-inch) piece fresh ginger (10g), grated

2 lime wedges

1 Place vermicelli in a large heatproof bowl, cover with boiling water; stand until tender; drain.
2 Place chicken, carrot, onion, cucumber, watermelon, coriander and mint in a large bowl; add vermicelli, toss to combine.
3 Combine sauces, the water and ginger in a small jug; season to taste. Toss dressing through salad. Serve with lime wedges.

tips If making the salad ahead of time, dress the salad just before serving. You could use thick rice noodles instead of the rice vermicelli.

nutritional count per serving
- 3g total fat
- 0.8g saturated fat
- 1335kJ (319 cal)
- 37.3g carbohydrate
- 32.8g protein
- 4g fibre

test kitchen tip

Pickled jalapeños chillies can be
found in the pickled vegetable or
Mexican section of supermarkets.

smoky orange prawn tacos

PREP + COOK TIME 30 MINUTES **SERVES** 2

20 uncooked peeled small king prawns (shrimp) (500g)

1 teaspoon smoked paprika

1 clove garlic, crushed

2 teaspoons fresh orange juice

cooking-oil spray

4 small white corn tortillas (100g)

2 tablespoons light sour cream

CORN SALSA

1 trimmed corn cob (250g)

1 medium tomato (150g), cut into wedges

1 small orange (180g), cut into segments

½ small red onion (50g), cut into wedges

2 tablespoons pickled jalapeño chillies

¼ cup loosely packed fresh coriander leaves (cilantro)

2 teaspoons lime juice

1 Place prawns, paprika, garlic and juice in a large bowl; mix to combine, season. Thread onto 20 bamboo skewers.
2 Make corn salsa.
3 Lightly spray a heated grill plate (or barbecue or grill) with oil; cook prawns for 3 minutes or until just changed in colour. Cook tortillas on a grill plate for 30 seconds each side. Fill tortillas with prawns and salsa; top with sour cream. Accompany with lime wedges, if you like.

corn salsa Cook corn on a heated grill plate (or grill or barbecue) for 10 minutes, turning occasionally. When cool enough to handle, use a sharp knife to remove the kernels from the cob. Combine corn in a medium bowl with remaining ingredients. Season to taste.

serving suggestion For a bit more of a 'kick', serve with 1 tablespoon of your favourite hot chilli sauce.

nutritional count per serving
▶ 10.1g total fat
▶ 3.7g saturated fat
▶ 2262kJ (540 cal)
▶ 44.6g carbohydrate
▶ 61.1g protein
▶ 11.1g fibre

diary entry

My favourite breakfast diet or otherwise. A hearty breakfast for men – the breakfast of champions. I wasn't keen on the quinoa salad for lunch, but it actually tasted pretty good. – David

Another amazing breakfast. I can't believe this is diet food. Even with a delicious lunch, I was hungry by 3pm, and couldn't say no to a piece of birthday pavlova at the office. – Kerry

bacon and baked beans on muffins

PREP + COOK TIME 30 MINUTES **SERVES** 2

cooking-oil spray

1 small brown onion (80g), chopped finely

2 cloves garlic, crushed

1 teaspoon sweet paprika

400g (12½ ounces) canned diced tomatoes

400g (12½ ounces) canned cannellini beans, rinsed, drained

1 tablespoon worcestershire sauce

4 thin low-fat shortcut bacon slices (80g)

2 multigrain english muffins (130g), split, toasted

2 tablespoons fresh baby basil leaves

1 Lightly spray a heated small non-stick saucepan with oil; cook onion, garlic and paprika, stirring, over medium heat, for 5 minutes or until onion is tender.

2 Add tomatoes, beans and sauce. Cook for 10 minutes or until mixture thickens slightly. Season to taste.

3 Cook bacon in a medium non-stick frying pan, over high heat, for 2 minutes each side or until crisp.

4 Top muffin halves with bacon and beans; sprinkle with basil to serve.

nutritional count per serving
▶ 8.5g total fat
▶ 2.5g saturated fat
▶ 1639kJ (391 cal)
▶ 44.3g carbohydrate
▶ 26.3g protein
▶ 11.7g fibre

test kitchen tips

For a vegetarian option, replace the bacon with low-fat cottage cheese. If you can't find baby basil leaves, just roughly chop larger leaves.

balsamic-roasted pumpkin and red quinoa salad

PREP + COOK TIME 45 MINUTES **SERVES** 2

500g (1 pound) jap pumpkin, cut into thin wedges

1 medium red onion (170g), cut into wedges

cooking-oil spray

2 tablespoons balsamic vinegar

½ cup (100g) red quinoa, rinsed, drained

1 cup (250ml) water

60g (2 ounces) mesclun

100g (3 ounces) mixed medley tomatoes, halved

50g (1½ ounces) low-fat ricotta, crumbled

½ cup fresh mint leaves

1 medium lemon (140g)

1 Preheat oven to 200°C/400°F. Line oven tray with baking paper. Place pumpkin and onion on tray; lightly spray with oil, season. Roast for 25 minutes. Drizzle with vinegar; roast for a further 10 minutes.

2 Meanwhile, place quinoa and the water in a small saucepan. Bring to the boil, reduce heat to low; cook, covered, for 12 minutes or until tender. Drain, rinse under cold water; drain.

3 Combine quinoa in a large bowl with pumpkin mixture, mesclun, tomato, ricotta and mint. Serve with a squeeze of lemon.

tips Red quinoa (pronounced keen-wa), is the seed of a leafy plant similar to spinach. Quinoa is gluten-free and has a delicate, slightly nutty taste and chewy texture; it is available from health food stores and in the health food aisle at larger supermarkets. You could also use white quinoa. Rinse it well before boiling. To take for lunch, make this recipe the day before, but keep the mesclun separate. Reheat the quinoa mixture at work, then mix through the mesclun. The salad can be served cold.

nutritional count per serving
- 15.8g total fat
- 52.9g carbohydrate
- 5.1g saturated fat
- 19.2g protein
- 1910kJ (456 cal)
- 12.5g fibre

nutritional count per serving
▸ 13g total fat
▸ 3.3g saturated fat
▸ 1482kJ (354 cal)
▸ 34.3g carbohydrate
▸ 21.5g protein
▸ 6g fibre

indian lamb wraps

PREP + COOK TIME 20 MINUTES **SERVES** 2

250g (8 ounces) lean minced (ground) lamb

1 tablespoon tandoori paste

cooking-oil spray

2 roti breads (95g)

1 small carrot (70g)

1 lebanese cucumber (130g)

1 tablespoon mango chutney

4 baby cos (romaine) lettuce leaves

2 tablespoons fresh coriander (cilantro) leaves

TANDOORI SAUCE

1½ tablespoons 99% fat-free mayonnaise

1½ tablespoons low-fat plain yoghurt

1 teaspoon tandoori paste

1 Combine lamb and paste in a medium bowl. Roll mixture into 10 balls.

2 Lightly spray a heated large non-stick frying pan with oil; cook meatballs, over medium heat, for 5 minutes or until cooked through. Remove from pan; cover to keep warm.

3 Cook roti in same pan for 1 minute each side or until heated through.

4 Make tandoori sauce.

5 Using a vegetable peeler, cut long strips from carrot and cucumber.

6 Spread roti with chutney; top with meatballs, carrot, cucumber, lettuce, coriander and tandoori sauce, roll to enclose.

tandoori sauce Combine ingredients in a small bowl.

tip You can serve the meatballs on naan or a wholemeal tortilla; but this will increase the kilojoules/calories slightly.

orange salad with chai-spiced syrup

PREP + COOK TIME 15 MINUTES (+ COOLING) **SERVES** 2

3 cardamom pods, bruised

2 tablespoons caster (superfine) sugar

⅓ cup (80ml) water

1 teaspoon fennel seeds

6 cloves

1 cinnamon stick

1 medium mandarin (200g), cut into wedges

1 small ruby grapefruit (350g), cut into segments

2 medium oranges (480g), sliced thinly

½ cup (140g) low-fat plain yoghurt

1 Place cardamom in a small saucepan with sugar, the water, fennel, cloves and cinnamon; bring to the boil, boil for 2 minutes. Remove from heat; cool.

2 Place mandarin, grapefruit and orange in a medium bowl. Spoon syrup over fruit; top with yoghurt, and sprinkle with orange rind, if you like.

tips Use a meat mallet to gently bruise the cardamom pod. If you don't have all the spices on hand, you can replace them with a chai black tea bag. Just strain the bag from the syrup after cooling for 15 minutes. Use blood oranges or plain grapefruit, if ruby grapefruit is unavailable. Discard the cinnamon stick before serving.

spiced mango chicken baguette

PREP TIME 10 MINUTES **SERVES** 2

160g (5 ounces) shredded cooked chicken

1 small mango (300g), sliced thinly

1 green onion (scallion), sliced thinly lengthways

1 teaspoon ground cumin

2 tablespoons extra-light spreadable cream cheese

2 tablespoons 99% fat-free mayonnaise

1 small wholemeal french breadstick (150g)

¼ cup fresh coriander (cilantro) sprigs

1 Combine chicken, mango and onion in a medium bowl. Whisk cumin, cream cheese and mayonnaise in a small bowl.

2 Cut baguette in half crossways; split each in half lengthways. Sandwich baguettes with mayonnaise, chicken mixture and coriander.

tips Use barbecued chicken breast with the skin removed, leftover roast chicken, or pan-fried or poached chicken breast. This would also be great in a sandwich made with multigrain bread.

diary entry

Breakfast was delicious, but I was hungry an hour before lunch. However, the baguette was well worth waiting for. – Kerry

nutritional count per serving

▶ 8.1g total fat

▶ 2.9g saturated fat

▶ 1868kJ (446 cal)

▶ 53.7g carbohydrate

▶ 35.3g protein

▶ 6.4g fibre

diary entry

The frittata really hit the spot for dinner; full of healthy vegetables, eggs and dotted with ricotta cheese, it was a substantial meal on which to end the day. – Pamela

ratatouille frittata

PREP + COOK TIME 30 MINUTES **SERVES** 2

You need an ovenproof frying pan as it goes under the grill; or cover the handle with a few layers of foil to protect it from the heat.

cooking-oil spray

1 small brown onion (80g), sliced thinly

1 small red capsicum (bell pepper) (150g), sliced thinly

½ small eggplant (115g), chopped finely

1 medium tomato (150g), cut into wedges

2 cloves garlic, sliced thinly

2 tablespoons fresh oregano leaves

2 eggs

4 egg whites

¼ cup (60ml) skim milk

2 tablespoons low-fat ricotta

2 slices wholemeal bread (90g), toasted

1 tablespoon basil pesto

60g (2 ounces) baby rocket leaves (arugula)

½ medium lemon (70g)

1 Lightly spray a medium non-stick frying pan with oil. Cook onion, capsicum, eggplant, tomato, garlic and half the oregano over medium heat for 10 minutes or until eggplant is cooked. Season to taste.

2 Whisk together eggs, egg whites and milk in a medium bowl. Pour over vegetables. Top with ricotta. Reduce heat to low, cook for 8 minutes.

3 Preheat grill (broiler). Cook frittata under the grill for 2 minutes or until just set.

4 Top frittata with remaining oregano. Spread toast with pesto, serve frittata on toast; accompany with rocket and a squeeze of lemon.

tip Freeze remaining bread to use in later recipes.

nutritional count per serving
▸ 13.6g total fat
▸ 3.4g saturated fat
▸ 1466kJ (350 cal)
▸ 30.2g carbohydrate
▸ 22.5g protein
▸ 8.7g fibre

diary entry

Loved the pancakes this morning, with maple syrup, yoghurt and berries – one of my favourite breakfasts so far. I also enjoyed the roll for lunch – it was so easy to put together in the morning before work. – Pamela

I wonder if I'm still losing weight on this diet. Most of the servings seem so large, but it's all healthy and all tastes so good, so I'm not complaining.
– Kerry

buckwheat pancakes with mixed berries

PREP + COOK TIME 20 MINUTES **SERVES** 2

¼ cup (35g) buckwheat flour

¼ cup (40g) wholemeal plain (all-purpose) flour

½ teaspoon baking powder

1 egg

½ cup (125ml) skim milk

1 tablespoon dark agave syrup

1 teaspoon vanilla extract

2 teaspoons finely grated lemon rind

cooking-oil spray

½ cup (140g) low-fat vanilla yoghurt

1 cup (150g) mixed fresh berries

1 tablespoon dark agave syrup, extra

1 Combine sifted flours and baking powder in a medium bowl.

2 Whisk together egg, milk, syrup, vanilla and lemon in a bowl. Add to flour mixture; stir until just combined.

3 Lightly spray a heated large non-stick frying pan with oil; cook ¼-cups of mixture, over medium heat, for 2 minutes each side or until browned and cooked through. Repeat to make a total of four pancakes.

4 Serve pancakes topped with yoghurt and berries; drizzle with extra syrup.

nutritional count per serving
▶ 5g total fat
▶ 1.3g saturated fat
▶ 1588kJ (379 cal)
▶ 67g carbohydrate
▶ 13.8g protein
▶ 5.4g fibre

50

test kitchen tips

Agave is available in the health food aisle of major supermarkets or health food stores. Substitute agave syrup with pure maple syrup, if you like. You could add your favourite spice, such as cinnamon or mixed spice, to the pancake mix. Thawed frozen berries can be used instead of the fresh berries.

roast beef and herbed cream cheese rolls

PREP TIME 10 MINUTES **SERVES** 2

⅓ cup (80g) extra-light spreadable cream cheese

1 tablespoon finely chopped fresh chives

2 teaspoons finely chopped fresh dill

2 medium multigrain rolls (100g)

2 teaspoons dijon mustard

4 slices rare roast beef (80g)

6 slices canned beetroot (beets) (80g)

1 medium tomato (150g), sliced thinly

20g (¾ ounce) rocket leaves (arugula)

1 Combine cream cheese and herbs in a small bowl; season to taste.
2 Split rolls in half. Spread roll bases with cheese mixture; spread tops with mustard. Sandwich rolls with beef, beetroot, tomato and rocket.

tip You could use pastrami, shaved turkey or chicken breast instead of the beef.

diary entry

I really liked lunch, simple but tasty. And dinner was good too; another filling meal so I didn't feel like snacking later in the evening. And, my stomach is feeling slightly flatter! – David

nutritional count per serving

▶ 9.2g total fat
▶ 28.4g carbohydrate
▶ 4.6g saturated fat
▶ 19g protein
▶ 1190kJ (284 cal)
▶ 5.4g fibre

nutritional count per serving
▶ 9.5g total fat
▶ 3.3g saturated fat
▶ 1968kJ (470 cal)
▶ 53.7g carbohydrate
▶ 35.8g protein
▶ 11.6g fibre

turkey chilli con carne filled kumara

PREP + COOK TIME 20 MINUTES **SERVES** 2

2 small kumara (orange sweet potato) (500g)

cooking-oil spray

200g (6½ ounces) minced (ground) turkey

1 small brown onion (80g), chopped finely

2 cloves garlic, crushed

2 teaspoons ground cumin

½ teaspoon chilli flakes

400g (12½ ounces) canned diced tomatoes

125g (4 ounces) canned kidney beans, rinsed, drained

2 teaspoons caster (superfine) sugar

¼ cup (20g) finely grated parmesan

60g (2 ounces) rocket leaves (arugula)

1 medium lemon (140g)

1 Prick kumara all over with a fork. Microwave on MEDIUM HIGH (75%) for 8 minutes or until tender.
2 Meanwhile, lightly spray a medium non-stick frying pan with oil; cook turkey, onion, garlic, cumin and chilli over high heat for 5 minutes, breaking up any lumps with a wooden spoon, until browned.
3 Add tomatoes, beans and sugar to pan; reduce heat to low. Cook for 5 minutes or until mixture is thickened.
4 Cut the kumara in half lengthways. Spoon the chilli con carne over kumara, sprinkle with parmesan. Serve with rocket and a squeeze of lemon.

tip Kumara can be baked in a moderate oven (180°C/350°F) for about 1 hour or until tender.

SHOPPING LIST

FRIDGE

- 30g baby bocconcini
- 1 tub reduced-fat cottage cheese
- 40g reduced-fat ricotta
- 1 tub reduced-fat spreadable cream cheese
- 8 eggs
- 600ml buttermilk
- 500ml skim milk
- 200g low-fat plain yoghurt
- 2 x 200g skim-milk fruit flavoured yoghurt
- 1 small bottle fresh apple juice
- 1 packet frozen broad beans
- 1 small packet frozen mixed berries

FRUIT

- 1 large green apple
- 2 medium green apples
- 250g cherries
- 400g honeydew melon
- 2 medium lemons
- 2 limes
- 2 nectarines
- 1 large orange
- 4 medium oranges
- 2 small peaches
- 125g punnet raspberries

VEGETABLES

- 340g asparagus
- 2 baby buk choy
- 1 packet bean sprouts
- 500g baby beetroots
- 1 small beetroot
- ¼ savoy cabbage
- ¼ wombok
- 1 large red capsicum
- 1 large carrot
- 5 small carrots
- ½ bunch celery
- 1 small red thai chilli
- 500g baby choy sum
- 1 small fennel
- 1 lebanese cucumber
- 3 cloves garlic
- 35g piece ginger
- 1 large brown onion
- 1 small brown onion
- 1 medium red onion
- 3 green onions
- 60g fresh shelled peas
- 1 large potato
- 200g butternut pumpkin
- 1 small radicchio
- 80g baby rocket leaves
- 1 bunch rocket leaves
- 300g mixed salad leaves
- 80g snow peas
- 50g baby spinach
- 350g cherry truss tomatoes
- 2 medium zucchini
- 1 small zucchini

HERBS

- 2 bunches chives
- 1 bunch coriander
- 1 bunch dill
- 1 bunch flat-leaf parsley
- 1 bunch mint
- 1 bunch thai basil

MEAT

- 100g beef fillet
- 350g lean minced beef
- 200g chicken breast fillet
- 6 (300g) french-trimmed lamb cutlets
- 220g pork fillet
- 50g shaved ham
- 80g sliced pastrami

SEAFOOD

- 100g hot-smoked trout

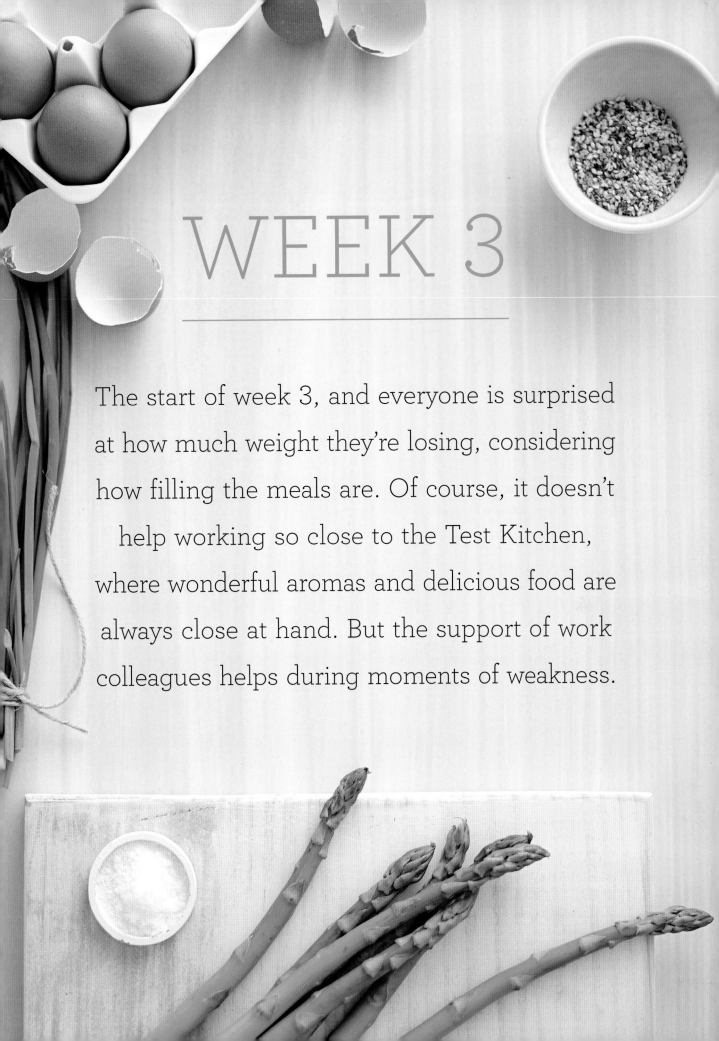

WEEK 3

The start of week 3, and everyone is surprised at how much weight they're losing, considering how filling the meals are. Of course, it doesn't help working so close to the Test Kitchen, where wonderful aromas and delicious food are always close at hand. But the support of work colleagues helps during moments of weakness.

asparagus with poached egg and dukkah

PREP + COOK TIME 10 MINUTES SERVES 2

170g (5½ ounces) asparagus, trimmed, halved lengthways

1 tablespoon white wine vinegar

2 eggs

2 slices wholemeal bread (90g), toasted

1 teaspoon almond dukkah

2 teaspoons finely chopped fresh chives

1 Half fill a large deep saucepan with water; bring to the boil. Add asparagus; cook for 2 minutes or until bright green and just tender. Transfer to a plate; cover to keep warm.

2 Add vinegar to water in pan and return to the boil. Break one egg into a cup then slide into pan; repeat with remaining egg. When both eggs are in the pan, return to the boil. Cover pan, turn off heat; stand for 3 minutes or until a light film of egg white sets over the yolks.

3 Place toast on serving plates. Top with asparagus and egg; sprinkle with dukkah and chives to serve.

diary entry

I was sensible with my eating choices over the weekend to make up for the extra food I ate last week because of work commitments. So, to find breakfast was a poached egg was a real treat. The dukkah adds a punchy flavour to the egg and asparagus, and I felt really satisfied at the end of it. – Fran

A family gathering put paid to good intensions over the weekend, so I was pleased to get back to eating healthy today. Mind you, it only lasted until lunchtime, when I had to attend a work function. I felt that by eating the sticky pork stir-fry for dinner, I didn't throw away all the good work of the previous 2 weeks. – Pamela

test kitchen tips

Use your favourite bread, toasted english muffin or bagel halves, if you like. You can use plain white vinegar, if that's what's in your pantry cupboard. Use a wooden spoon to make a whirlpool in the water before adding the egg, if you like; however, it's best to poach just one egg at a time this way, as it gets a bit tricky whirlpooling the water once there's more than one egg in it.

nutritional count per serving
- ▶ 7.8g total fat
- ▶ 1.9g saturated fat
- ▶ 852kJ (203 cal)
- ▶ 18.2g carbohydrate
- ▶ 12.9g protein
- ▶ 3.7g fibre

test kitchen tips

Remove the seeds and membranes from the chilli for a milder heat. You can use shredded barbecue chicken breast (without the skin) instead of the tuna. Add your favourite vegetables, such as bean sprouts, capsicum or cucumber. Keep the rolls moist by covering them with slightly damp kitchen paper, then store them in an airtight container in the fridge.

tuna rice paper rolls

PREP TIME 20 MINUTES **SERVES** 2

50g (1½ ounces) rice vermicelli

6 x 22cm (9-inch) rice paper rounds

185g (5½ ounces) canned tuna in springwater, drained, flaked

1 small carrot (70g), cut into matchsticks

½ cup (40g) finely shredded wombok (napa cabbage)

¼ cup loosely packed fresh coriander leaves (cilantro)

1 tablespoon light soy sauce

1 tablespoon rice vinegar

1½ teaspoons caster (superfine) sugar

1 green onion (scallion), sliced thinly

1 fresh small red thai (serrano) chilli, chopped finely

1 Place vermicelli in a large heatproof bowl; cover with boiling water. Stand until just tender; drain. Using kitchen scissors, cut vermicelli coarsely.

2 Dip one rice paper round into a bowl of warm water until soft. Lift sheet from water; place on a clean tea towel. Top with one-sixth of the vermicelli, tuna, carrot and wombok; top with coriander. Fold sheet over filling, then fold in both sides. Continue rolling to enclose filling. Repeat with remaining ingredients to make a total of six rolls.

3 Combine soy sauce, vinegar, sugar, onion and chilli in a small bowl; stir until sugar dissolves. Accompany rolls with sauce.

nutritional count per serving
▶ 2.4g total fat
▶ 0.7g saturated fat
▶ 840kJ (200 cal)
▶ 21.3g carbohydrate
▶ 21.5g protein
▶ 3.4g fibre

sticky pork stir-fry

PREP + COOK TIME 35 MINUTES **SERVES** 2

⅓ cup (65g) brown rice

2 tablespoons sweet chilli sauce

2 teaspoons light soy sauce

1 tablespoon brown sugar

cooking-oil spray

220g (7 ounces) pork fillet, sliced thinly

1 medium red onion (170g), cut into wedges

1 large red capsicum (bell pepper) (350g), sliced thinly

6cm (2½-inch) piece fresh ginger (30g), cut into matchsticks

½ cup thai basil leaves

500g (1 pound) baby choy sum, cut into 10cm (4-inch) lengths

1 Cook rice in a large saucepan of boiling water, uncovered, for 30 minutes or until tender. Drain.
2 Meanwhile, combine sauces and sugar in a small jug; stir until sugar dissolves.
3 Lightly spray a heated wok with oil; stir-fry pork and onion, in three batches, over high heat, for 2 minutes or until browned.
4 Return pork mixture to the wok with capsicum and ginger; stir-fry for 2 minutes or until capsicum is tender. Remove from heat. Add half the basil and toss to combine.
5 Place choy sum in a heatproof bowl; cover with boiling water, drain well.
6 Spoon rice and choy sum between serving plates. Top with stir-fry mixture; sprinkle with remaining basil.

nutritional count per serving
▶ 5.9g total fat
▶ 1.3g saturated fat
▶ 1776kJ (424 cal)
▶ 52.6g carbohydrate
▶ 34.5g protein
▶ 10.8g fibre

test kitchen tips

Use vegetables of your choice such as green beans, snow peas or buk choy. Use sliced chicken breast or thinly sliced beef rump steak as an alternative to the pork fillet. Use regular basil if thai basil is unavailable.

diary entry

My favourite meal of the day was the stir-fry for dinner. I felt like I was eating out at my local Thai restaurant – the flavours were perfect, and reminded me of too many takeaway meals. – David

raspberry and pistachio bircher muesli

PREP TIME 10 MINUTES (+ REFRIGERATION) SERVES 2

Start this recipe the night before.

1 medium green apple (150g), unpeeled

1 cup (90g) rolled oats

⅓ cup (80ml) fresh apple juice

⅓ cup (95g) low-fat plain yoghurt

¼ teaspoon vanilla bean paste

60g (2 ounces) fresh or frozen raspberries

1 tablespoon pistachios, sliced thinly

1 Halve and core unpeeled apple; cut one half into matchsticks. Wrap other apple half in plastic wrap and refrigerate until needed (rub the surface with a little lemon juice to stop it from browning, if you like). Combine oats, juice, yoghurt, vanilla and apple matchsticks in a small bowl. Cover with plastic wrap; refrigerate overnight.

2 The next morning, cut remaining apple half into matchsticks (or cut into a small dice). Gently fold half the raspberries into the oat mixture; sprinkle with the apple, raspberries and nuts to serve.

tips The apple is left unpeeled for a little extra fibre, and also looks pretty with the flecks of green against the red raspberries. Drizzle the muesli with a teaspoon of honey or pure maple syrup for a weekend treat. Don't add too much as it will affect your kilojoules/calories. For a citrus twist, add a little finely grated orange rind and replace the apple juice with orange juice. Replace the raspberries with blueberries and sprinkle with lightly roasted hazelnuts.

nutritional count per serving
▶ 7.9g total fat
▶ 1.2g saturated fat
▶ 1242kJ (297 cal)
▶ 42.2g carbohydrate
▶ 9.8g protein
▶ 8g fibre

open reuben sandwich

PREP TIME 15 MINUTES **SERVES** 2

1 small beetroot (beet) (100g), peeled, cut into matchsticks

1 small carrot (70g), cut into matchsticks

¾ cup (60g) finely shredded cabbage

1 tablespoon low-fat plain yoghurt

2 teaspoons dijon mustard

2 thick slices rye bread (100g), toasted

4 slices pastrami (80g)

1 small pickled cucumber (60g), sliced thinly lengthways

1 tablespoon dill sprigs

1 Combine beetroot, carrot and cabbage in a large bowl. Add yoghurt and mustard; toss gently to combine. Season to taste.

2 Top bread with pastrami, beetroot mixture and pickled cucumber; sprinkle with dill.

tips You could use turkey pastrami as an alternative and add 2 teaspoons of cranberry sauce to the coleslaw. Use your favourite wrap or bread instead of rye bread. If taking to work for lunch, package coleslaw in a separate container and assemble the sandwich just before eating. If you have one, use a mandoline to cut the vegetables into matchsticks, or you can coarsely grate them.

nutritional count per serving
▶ 2.9g total fat
▶ 0.7g saturated fat
▶ 1039kJ (248 cal)
▶ 37g carbohydrate
▶ 14.5g protein
▶ 7.4g fibre

test kitchen tips

You can use a lamb backstrap instead of cutlets, cook for 3-4 minutes each side and then slice thickly. If fresh broad beans are in season, you can use them instead of frozen ones.

sumac lamb cutlets with pea salad

PREP + COOK TIME 20 MINUTES **SERVES** 2

1½ cups (225g) frozen broad beans (fava beans), partially thawed, peeled

½ cup (60g) fresh or frozen peas

80g (2½ ounces) snow peas, trimmed

60g (2 ounces) baby rocket leaves (arugula)

1 tablespoon thinly sliced preserved lemon rind

2 tablespoons low-fat plain yoghurt

cooking-oil spray

1 teaspoon cumin seeds

6 french-trimmed lamb cutlets (300g)

1 teaspoon sumac

1 Cook beans in a large saucepan of boiling water for 1 minute. Add peas and snow peas; return to the boil, simmer for 1 minute or until snow peas are bright green and tender. Refresh under cold running water; drain. Transfer to a large bowl.

2 Toss rocket and half the preserved lemon rind into bean mixture; season to taste. Combine yoghurt and remaining rind in a small bowl.

3 Lightly spray a heated large non-stick frying pan with oil; cook cumin seeds, stirring over high heat, for 30 seconds or until fragrant. Transfer seeds to a small bowl.

4 Remove excess fat from lamb. Sprinkle sumac evenly over lamb; season. Cook lamb in same frying pan, over medium high, for 2 minutes each side or until cooked to your liking. Remove from heat; cover to keep warm.

5 Toss cumin seeds into pea salad. Serve lamb with salad and yoghurt mixture. Accompany with lemon cheeks, if you like.

diary entry

The bircher muesli was really delicious, and filling too, so it's a good meal to start the day, keeping snacking at bay. While I love lamb cutlets, I was a little hungry after dinner. I could easily have eaten more than the three cutlets allocated for this meal, as they are quite tiny. – Fran

Didn't feel hungry after the muesli for breakfast; it was so filling and gave me the energy to get through my morning's work. At lunch I particularly enjoyed the beetroot slaw on the reuben sandwich. Any meal with peas and broad beans makes my hit list – I love them; this dinner is a new favourite. – Pamela

nutritional count per serving
▶ 20.5g total fat
▶ 8.4g saturated fat
▶ 1489kJ (356 cal)
▶ 13.2g carbohydrate
▶ 26.4g protein
▶ 6.6g fibre

tomato and rocket bruschetta

PREP + COOK TIME 15 MINUTES **SERVES** 2

250g (8 ounces) cherry truss tomatoes

cooking-oil spray

⅓ cup (65g) reduced-fat cottage cheese

1 tablespoon finely chopped fresh chives

2 teaspoons finely chopped fresh dill

2 thick slices soy and quinoa bread (100g), toasted

20g (¾ ounces) rocket leaves (arugula)

1 Preheat grill (broiler). Line an oven tray with baking paper.
2 Place tomatoes on tray; lightly spray with oil, season. Grill for 5 minutes or until tomatoes begin to collapse.
3 Combine cheese and herbs in a small bowl; season with pepper.
4 Spread cottage cheese mixture over bread slices; top with rocket and tomatoes.

tips To make this recipe even faster, roughly chop the tomatoes instead of grilling. Replace the dill with basil and add a little garlic. You could use sliced ciabatta, or any leftover frozen bread, if you prefer.

nutritional count per serving
▶ 8g total fat
▶ 2g saturated fat
▶ 1022kJ (244 cal)
▶ 29.8g carbohydrate
▶ 11g protein
▶ 5.6g fibre

nutritional count per serving
▶ 3.8g total fat
▶ 1.3g saturated fat
▶ 891kJ (213 cal)
▶ 17.8g carbohydrate
▶ 22.4g protein
▶ 6.9g fibre

diary entry

Ever since the stir-fry on Monday night, I've been craving takeaway Asian food; thank goodness for this delicious soup. – David

asian beef and noodle soup

PREP + COOK TIME 30 MINUTES (+ FREEZING) **SERVES** 2

100g (3 ounce) beef fillet

2 cups (500ml) beef consommé

1 cup (250ml) water

2 star anise

1 cinnamon stick

2 baby buk choy (300g), sliced thinly lengthways

1 tablespoon lime juice

2 teaspoons fish sauce

50g (1½ ounces) rice stick noodles

1 cup (80g) bean sprouts

¼ cup loosely packed fresh coriander sprigs (cilantro sprigs)

¼ cup loosely packed fresh mint sprigs

2 green onions (scallions), cut into matchsticks

1 fresh small red thai (serrano) chilli, sliced thinly

1 lime

1 Cook beef in a medium frying pan, over medium high heat, turning, for 2 minutes or until seared. Cool, then wrap beef in plastic wrap, place in the freezer for 1 hour or until firm. Unwrap; use a sharp knife to thinly slice beef.

2 Combine consommé, the water and spices in a medium saucepan over high heat; bring to the boil. Reduce heat; simmer stock for 15 minutes.

3 Add buk choy, lime juice and sauce to stock; remove from heat, stand for 3 minutes or until buk choy is just tender.

4 Place noodles in a large heatproof bowl; cover with boiling water. Stand until just tender; drain.

5 Divide noodles and beef slices among serving bowls; pour over hot stock mixture with buk choy. Sprinkle with sprouts, herbs, onion and chilli. Serve with a squeeze of lime.

test kitchen tips

Replace the chicken with pork
fillet or salmon. Use a mandoline
to cut the fennel into paper thin
slices. You can substitute fresh
baby beetroot with canned baby
beets, if you like.

roasted beetroot, orange and char-grilled chicken salad

PREP + COOK TIME 45 MINUTES (+ STANDING) **SERVES** 2

You need two oranges for this recipe – one for the salad and one for the juice.

500g (1 pound) baby beetroots (beets), leaves trimmed

1 chicken breast fillet (200g)

cooking-oil spray

1 large orange (300g)

1 tablespoon orange juice

2 teaspoons wholegrain mustard

1 teaspoon olive oil

½ teaspoon fennel seeds, toasted

1 small fennel bulb (200g), sliced thinly

1 small radicchio (150g), leaves torn

1 tablespoon toasted slivered almonds

1 Preheat oven to 180°C/375°F. Wrap each beetroot in pieces of foil; place on an oven tray. Roast for 30 minutes or until tender. Stand for 15 minutes or until cooled slightly. Peel beetroots; cut in half.

2 Meanwhile, heat a grill plate (or barbecue or grill). Lightly spray chicken with oil; season. Cook for 4 minutes each side or until golden brown and just cooked through. Cover; rest for 5 minutes, then slice thickly.

3 Finely grate orange rind. Peel orange; use a small knife to cut orange crossways into thin slices. Place into a large bowl.

4 To make the dressing, combine juice with mustard, oil and seeds in a small jug; season.

5 Add beetroot, fennel and radicchio to bowl with orange slices; drizzle with dressing, toss gently to combine.

6 Top salad with chicken; sprinkle over nuts and rind.

tip Use golden beetroots for a colourful alternative if in season.

nutritional count per serving
▶ 13.3g total fat
▶ 2.5g saturated fat
▶ 1681kJ (402 cal)
▶ 33.5g carbohydrate
▶ 30.4g protein
▶ 14.3g fibre

nutritional count per serving
- ▶ 9.9g total fat
- ▶ 2.9g saturated fat
- ▶ 1104kJ (264 cal)
- ▶ 20.2g carbohydrate
- ▶ 21.6g protein
- ▶ 3.2g fibre

breakfast frittata

PREP + COOK TIME 15 MINUTES **SERVES** 2

2 eggs

2 egg whites

2 green onions (scallions), sliced thinly diagonally

cooking-oil spray

170g (5½ ounces) asparagus

50g (1½ ounces) shaved ham, sliced thinly

1 tablespoon reduced-fat ricotta, crumbled

2 slices multigrain bread (90g), toasted

1 Preheat oven to 180°C/375°F. Lightly spray a small (15cm/6-inch) ovenproof dish with oil.

2 Whisk egg, egg whites and onion in a small bowl until well combined; season.

3 Reserve half the asparagus, thinly slice remaining asparagus diagonally. Arrange sliced asparagus and ham in pan. Pour over egg mixture, sprinkle with ricotta and top with remaining asparagus spears.

4 Bake for 10 minutes or until golden and just set. Cut frittata into wedges; serve with toast; sprinkle with parsley leaves, if you like.

tip If you don't have a frying pan with a lid, cover the pan with foil or a scone tray.

hot-smoked trout, apple and celery salad

PREP TIME 15 MINUTES **SERVES** 2

1 tablespoon finely grated lemon rind

2 teaspoons lemon juice

2 teaspoons hot water

1 teaspoon dijon mustard

1 teaspoon olive oil

2 stalks celery (300g), trimmed, sliced thinly diagonally

300g (9½ ounces) mixed salad leaves

1 large granny smith apple (200g), cored, sliced thinly crossways

100g (3 ounces) hot-smoked trout, flaked coarsely

2 x 1cm (½-inch) slices sourdough (55g), toasted

1 To make dressing, combine juice, the water, mustard and oil in a small jug. Season to taste.

2 Combine celery, salad leaves, apple and trout in a large bowl; drizzle with dressing, toss gently.

3 To serve, sprinkle salad with rind; accompany with sourdough.

tips Use a zesting tool to remove the rind from the lemon. Replace the lemon juice and rind with orange for a sweeter, more subtle citrus flavour. We used red witlof for added colour, but use your favourite salad mix. Use hot-smoked salmon or shredded barbecued chicken breast as an alternative. Freeze any leftover sourdough to use in future recipes.

diary entry

Lunch was a winner for me – the smoked trout has good flavour and teams well with the crunch of the apple and celery. – Pamela

nutritional count per serving

▶ 6g total fat

▶ 1g saturated fat

▶ 1045kJ (250 cal)

▶ 27.1g carbohydrate

▶ 18.7g protein

▶ 6.7g fibre

cottage pie

PREP + COOK TIME 45 MINUTES **SERVES** 2

cooking-oil spray

1 large brown onion (200g), chopped finely

1 large carrot (180g), chopped finely

1 trimmed stalk celery (100g), chopped finely

2 cloves garlic, crushed

250g (8 ounces) lean minced (ground) beef

400g (12½ ounces) canned diced tomatoes

1 tablespoon worcestershire sauce

1 large potato (300g)

200g (6½ ounces) butternut pumpkin, chopped coarsely

20g (¾ ounce) low-fat spreadable cream cheese

1 tablespoon finely chopped fresh chives

1 Preheat oven to 220°C/425°F.

2 Meanwhile, spray a large saucepan with oil; add onion, carrot, celery and garlic. Cook on stove top, stirring over high heat, for 5 minutes or until onion softens.

3 Add beef; cook, stirring, for 5 minutes. Add tomato and sauce; reduce to a simmer. Simmer, stirring occasionally, for 15 minutes or until beef mixture thickens. Season to taste.

4 Meanwhile, cook potato and pumpkin in a large saucepan of boiling water for 15 minutes or until tender; drain. Return to pan; mash until smooth. Add cream cheese; stir to combine, season to taste.

5 Spoon beef mixture into a 4-cup (1-litre) ovenproof pan. Top with pumpkin mash.

6 Bake for 10 minutes or until heated through. Sprinkle with chives, and serve with rocket leaves, if you like.

diary entry

Today's recipes were really filling thanks to the protein from the eggs, fish and beef; protein tends to take the edge off hunger pangs. The frittata was a good way to start the day. If you feel full, you won't reach for a biscuit, and are more likely to stay focussed on the diet. The tasty cottage pie would meet with approval from the family. – Fran

I've been having a bad week, so I went out and had a big fry-up for breakfast; needless to say, I was still full at lunchtime. Dinner was just what I needed to get back on track. This hearty cottage pie is packed full of flavour. I can't believe it is low-calorie. – Kerry

nutritional count per serving

▶ 14.4g total fat	▶ 39.8g carbohydrate
▶ 5.8g saturated fat	▶ 42.6g protein
▶ 2045kJ (489 cal)	▶ 13.9g fibre

test kitchen tips

If you are in a hurry, roughly chop the onion, celery and carrot, then process together until finely chopped. Use lamb mince to make a shepherd's pie and flavour it with chopped mint.

orange, cranberry and walnut muffins

PREP + COOK TIME 30 MINUTES MAKES 6

1 large orange (300g), unpeeled

1 cup (150g) self-raising flour

1 cup (160g) wholemeal self-raising flour

⅔ cup (150g) firmly packed brown sugar

¼ cup (35g) dried cranberries

2 tablespoons coarsely chopped walnuts

1 cup (250ml) buttermilk

1 egg

2 tablespoons vegetable oil

2 teaspoons finely grated orange rind

¼ cup (60ml) orange juice

1 Preheat oven to 180°C/375°F. Grease a 6-hole (¾-cup/180ml) texas muffin pan.
2 Use a vegetable peeler to peel six strips of rind from the orange.
3 Combine sifted flours, sugar, cranberries and nuts in a large bowl; make a well in the centre.
4 Whisk buttermilk, egg, oil, rind and juice in a medium jug; pour into centre of flour mixture. Stir until just combined (don't over-mix).
5 Spoon mixture evenly among pan holes; push the orange strips into top of mixture. Bake for 20 minutes or until lightly golden. Serve warm or at room temperature.

tips See if you can get the 6 orange strips and 2 teaspoons of rind from 1 orange, otherwise you may need to buy 2 small oranges. This recipe makes 6 — freeze the remaining 4 muffins for later use.

nutritional count per muffin (1 serving consists of one muffin)

▶ 10.9g total fat   ▶ 65.8g carbohydrate
▶ 1.8g saturated fat   ▶ 9.4g protein
▶ 1692kJ (404 cal)   ▶ 4.7g fibre

zucchini and green olive pizza

PREP + COOK TIME 30 MINUTES **SERVES** 2

2 tablespoons reduced-fat ricotta

2 wholemeal pitta pockets (160g)

2 medium zucchini (240g), sliced thinly into ribbons

100g (3 ounces) cherry medley tomatoes, sliced thinly

30g (1 ounce) baby bocconcini, torn coarsely

4 pimento-stuffed olives, sliced thinly

20g (4 ounces) baby spinach leaves

1 Preheat oven to 200°C/400°F.
2 Spread ricotta over each pitta; top with zucchini, tomato, bocconcini and olives.
3 Bake for 12 minutes or until heated through. Top with spinach to serve.

tips When in season, use yellow zucchini for added colour, and sprinkle with black olives or capers. If taking to work for lunch, prepare the pizza, wrap in baking paper and cook in a heated sandwich press until the base is crisp and heated through.

diary entry

Unfortunately, while the muffin was tasty, I didn't find it very filling for breakfast, especially after yesterday's frittata – but that's why there are snacks at the back of this book, for those times when you're hungry, but don't want to break the diet. I found the pizza for lunch a lot more filling. – Fran

nutritional count per serving
▶ 7.8g total fat
▶ 41.8g carbohydrate
▶ 3.8g saturated fat
▶ 14.5g protein
▶ 1308kJ (313 cal)
▶ 8.1g fibre

test kitchen tips

Use a zesting tool to remove the lemon rind. Replace the dried lentils with canned lentils or borlotti beans.

lentil and paprika meatball minestrone

PREP + COOK TIME 35 MINUTES **SERVES** 2

100g (3 ounces) lean minced (ground) beef

1 teaspoon smoked paprika

½ teaspoon ground cumin

cooking-oil spray

1 small brown onion (80g), chopped finely

1 small carrot (70g), chopped finely

1 trimmed stalk celery (100g), chopped finely

1 small zucchini (90g), chopped finely

400g (12½ ounces) canned diced tomatoes

2 cups (500ml) chicken stock

⅓ cup (65g) french-style lentils

GREMOLATA

1 clove garlic, sliced thinly

1 tablespoon fresh flat-leaf parsley leaves

2 teaspoons finely grated lemon rind

1 Combine mince, paprika and cumin in a small bowl. Roll teaspoons of mixture into balls. Lightly spray a large saucepan with oil; cook meatballs, over high heat, turning occasionally, for 2 minutes or until golden. Transfer to a bowl.

2 Add onion, carrot, celery and zucchini to same pan; cook, stirring, for 4 minutes or until onion softens. Add tomato, stock, lentils and meatballs; bring to the boil. Reduce heat to medium; cook, covered, for 20 minutes or until lentils are tender. Season to taste.

3 Meanwhile, make gremolata; sprinkle over minestrone to serve.

gremolata Preheat grill (broiler). Line an oven tray with paper. Place garlic on tray; gently grill for 2 minutes or until golden on both sides. Combine with parsley and lemon.

nutritional count per serving
▶ 8.2g total fat
▶ 2.4g saturated fat
▶ 1253kJ (299 cal)
▶ 26.1g carbohydrate
▶ 25.4g protein
▶ 11.6g fibre

SHOPPING LIST

FRIDGE

- 1 small tub light chive and onion cream cheese
- 1 small tub reduced-fat cottage cheese
- 25g reduced-fat fetta
- 1 small block parmesan
- 100g reduced-fat ricotta
- 8 eggs
- 600ml buttermilk
- 300ml skim milk
- 2 x 200g low-fat plain yoghurt
- 1 small packet frozen corn kernels
- 1 packet fillo pastry
- 1 small packet frozen peas
- 1 small packet frozen raspberries

FRUIT

- 2 small apples
- 1 large banana
- 2 small bananas
- 250g green grapes
- 3 medium lemons
- 1 lime
- 1 medium mango
- 1 small pear
- 400g watermelon

VEGETABLES

- 1 small avocado
- 340g asparagus
- 85g broccoli
- 175g broccolini
- 100g green beans
- 1 large red capsicum
- 1 large carrot
- 375g cauliflower
- 3 sticks celery
- 1 fresh long green chilli
- 1 corn cob
- 2 lebanese cucumbers
- 1 small eggplant
- 1 baby fennel
- 1 small fennel
- 4 cloves garlic
- 25g piece ginger
- 400g kumara
- 1 small leek
- 3 small brown onions
- 3 green onions
- 1 small red onion
- 1 medium red onion
- 6 kipfler potatoes
- 350g butternut pumpkin
- 150g baby rocket leaves
- 180g baby spinach leaves
- 280g mixed tomato medley
- 200g red grape tomatoes

HERBS

- 1 bunch basil
- 1 bunch thai basil
- 2 bunches coriander
- 1 bunch flat-leaf parsley
- 1 bunch mint
- 1 bunch sage
- 1 stick lemon grass

MEAT

- ½ barbecued chicken
- 200g smoked chicken breast
- 250g chicken tenderloins
- 200g pork fillet
- 60g shaved ham
- 30g sliced prosciutto

SEAFOOD

- 2 x 120g ocean trout fillets
- 180g slices smoked salmon

WEEK 4

It's the last week, and it hasn't been a chore. Except for those times when life gets in the way, which it tends to do, everyone pretty much stuck to the eating plan. Don't feel guilty when temptation strikes: just get back on the eating plan the next day, and you're sure to achieve your new healthy lifestyle.

"diary entry

The final week begins! I had a pretty healthy weekend, and feel on track. I didn't need to snack at all today – must be the first time ever. The smoothie for breakfast was very filling and tasted so sweet. The snails were something different, but were very nice just the same. But my favourite was the seafood dinner. – David

I've lost 4kg already and am definitely feeling more energetic, mainly due to my new enthusiasm for exercise. I go to the gym with my daughter and I'm finding it really enjoyable. My clothes feel more comfortable, and people are starting to notice the weight loss, and that makes me feel good about myself too. – Fran"

banana and raspberry maple smoothie

PREP TIME 10 MINUTES **SERVES** 2 (MAKES 2½ CUPS)

1 large ripe banana (230g), chopped coarsely

1 cup (135g) frozen raspberries

¾ cup (210g) low-fat plain yoghurt

¾ cup (180ml) skim milk

2 teaspoons pure maple syrup

1 Blend or process ingredients until smooth. Pour between two serving glasses.

tips Replace raspberries with blueberries or strawberries, if you prefer. Add honey and ground cinnamon if desired. Add crushed ice to the blender for an even thicker smoothie.

nutritional count per serving

▶ 0.6g total fat
▶ 0.3g saturated fat
▶ 907kJ (217 cal)
▶ 35.7g carbohydrate
▶ 12.3g protein
▶ 5.8g fibre

moroccan eggplant and ricotta fillo snails

PREP + COOK TIME 40 MINUTES **SERVES** 2

cooking-oil spray

1 small eggplant (230g), diced into 2cm (¾-inch) cubes

1 small brown onion (80g) chopped coarsely

½ teaspoon each ground cumin, coriander, ginger, cinnamon and turmeric

150g (4½ ounces) well drained char-grilled capsicum (bell pepper), chopped coarsely

¼ cup (40g) reduced-fat ricotta

4 sheets fillo pastry

¼ teaspoon fennel seeds

200g (6½ ounces) mixed tomato medley, sliced thickly

½ cup mint leaves

¼ cup (70g) low-fat plain yoghurt

½ teaspoon sumac

1 Preheat oven to 200°C/400°F.

2 Lightly spray a large heated non-stick frying pan with oil; add eggplant and onion. Cook, stirring, over high heat, for 5 minutes or until onion softens. Add spices; cook for 1 minute or until fragrant. Remove from heat; cool slightly.

3 Combine eggplant mixture with capsicum and ricotta in a large bowl; toss to combine. Season to taste.

4 Line an oven tray with baking paper. Lightly spray one fillo sheet with oil; top with another sheet. Spoon half the eggplant mixture down one long side of the pastry. Roll pastry over filling to form a log (don't roll too tightly). Roll log into a spiral shape; place on tray, tucking end loosely under spiral. Repeat with remaining pastry and filling. Sprinkle with fennel seeds.

5 Bake snails for 20 minutes or until golden.

6 Meanwhile, combine tomato and mint leaves in a medium bowl. Combine yoghurt and half the sumac in a small bowl.

7 Serve snails warm or at room temperature, sprinkled with remaining sumac, and accompanied with tomato and mint, and yoghurt mixture.

tips You can make the filling the night before, and assemble the snails just before baking. If taking the pastries to work, store, covered with foil, in the fridge; bring to room temperature the next day.

nutritional count per serving
▶ 10.4g total fat
▶ 2g saturated fat
▶ 1125kJ (269 cal)
▶ 31.3g carbohydrate
▶ 11.4g protein
▶ 7.6g fibre

char-grilled trout with kipfler potato salad

PREP + COOK TIME 30 MINUTES **SERVES** 2

6 kipfler potatoes (fingerlings) (215g),
unpeeled, washed, sliced thickly diagonally

2 slices prosciutto (30g), halved lengthways

2 x 120g (4-ounce) ocean trout fillets

cooking-oil spray

170g (5½ ounces) asparagus, cut diagonally
into 5cm (2-inch) lengths

1 baby fennel bulb (130g), sliced thinly

80g (2½ ounces) baby rocket leaves (arugula)

2 teaspoons rinsed, drained baby capers

BUTTERMILK AND FENNEL DRESSING

¼ cup (60ml) buttermilk

2 teaspoons dijon mustard

2 teaspoons lemon juice

1 tablespoon finely chopped fennel fronds

1 Make buttermilk and fennel dressing.
2 Place potato in a medium saucepan, cover with cold water; bring to the boil. Boil for 10 minutes or until tender. Rinse under cold water. Drain.
3 Wrap prosciutto around fillets. Lightly spray a heated grill plate (or grill or barbecue) with oil; cook trout for 3 minutes each side or until cooked to your liking. Transfer to a plate, cover; rest for 5 minutes.
4 Cook potato and asparagus on the grill plate for 2 minutes or until lightly charred. Remove from heat.
5 Combine potato, asparagus, fennel, rocket and capers in a large bowl. Drizzle with dressing; toss gently to combine. Top potato salad with trout to serve.

buttermilk and fennel dressing Whisk ingredients in a small jug; season to taste.

---

nutritional count per serving
▶ 9.6g total fat
▶ 2.6g saturated fat
▶ 1302kJ (311 cal)
▶ 18.6g carbohydrate
▶ 34.4g protein
▶ 4.2g fibre

test kitchen tips

If you don't have a grill plate, you can cook the recipe in a large non-stick frying pan instead. Swap the trout for salmon, if you like. To bulk out the vegetable component of this dish, add some snow peas.

test kitchen tips

Replace the salmon with bacon,
trimmed of fat, or shaved ham,
if you like. Add some fresh herbs
such as chives or basil.

diary entry

The burrito takes me back to Cancun – it tasted just like the Mexican original. It doesn't really feel like I'm on a diet, it all tastes so good, and the portions are pretty substantial. Even the sandwich at lunch, while simple, kept me full all afternoon. – David

I loved the smoked salmon on the breakfast burrito, and while I didn't mind the smoky corn, I am not a fan of smoked chicken, so I used char-grilled chicken instead. Poached chicken would also work. – Fran

breakfast burrito

PREP + COOK TIME 10 MINUTES **SERVES** 2

2 eggs

2 egg whites

2 x 22cm (8¾-inch) wholegrain soft wraps

40g (1½ ounces) reduced-fat ricotta, crumbled

100g (3 ounces) smoked salmon

80g (2½ ounces) baby spinach leaves

1 medium lemon (130g), cut into wedges

1 Whisk eggs and egg whites in a medium bowl until combined; season.

2 Heat a medium non-stick frying pan; cook wraps, one at a time, on high heat, for 1 minute or until warm. Transfer to a plate; cover with foil to keep warm.

3 Add egg mixture to same heated pan; cook, stirring occasionally, for 2 minutes or until mixture is lightly scrambled and just set.

4 Spoon scrambled eggs over wraps; top with ricotta, salmon and spinach. Roll wrap to enclose filling. Serve immediately with lemon.

nutritional count per serving
▶ 10g total fat
▶ 3.3g saturated fat
▶ 968kJ (231 cal)
▶ 8.4g carbohydrate
▶ 26g protein
▶ 1.9g fibre

smoky corn, chicken and celery open sandwich

PREP + COOK TIME 15 MINUTES **SERVES** 2

cooking-oil spray

1 trimmed corn cob (250g)

¼ teaspoon smoked paprika

4 x 1cm (½-inch) thick slices dark rye bread (110g)

2 tablespoons low-fat plain yoghurt

1 smoked chicken breast fillet (200g), sliced thinly

1 trimmed celery stalk (100g), sliced thinly

1 green onion (scallion), sliced thinly lengthways

1 Heat a grill pan (grill or barbecue).

2 Lightly spray corn with oil, sprinkle with paprika; cook corn, turning, for 6 minutes or until tender. Cool slightly. Using a sharp knife, cut down the length of the corn cob to remove kernels.

3 Toast bread on a grill plate for 1 minute each side or until lightly toasted.

4 Spread a little of the yoghurt over 2 toast slices; layer chicken, celery, onion, corn and remaining yoghurt between remaining toast slices, season.

tips Add ground cumin and coriander to the corn for extra spice. You could swap the smoked chicken for poached chicken breast, if you like.

diary entry

I was still full from breakfast, so I turned this into a salad and had it without the bread. – Pamela

nutritional count per serving

▶ 6.5g total fat   ▶ 47.9g carbohydrate
▶ 1.3g saturated fat   ▶ 42.2g protein
▶ 1854kJ (467 cal)   ▶ 10.2g fibre

nutritional count per serving
▶ 10.2g total fat ▶ 19.5g carbohydrate
▶ 6.1g saturated fat ▶ 10.8g protein
▶ 1006kJ (240 cal) ▶ 14.3g fibre

cauliflower, pumpkin and pea curry

PREP + COOK TIME 30 MINUTES **SERVES** 2

cooking-oil spray

1 small brown onion (80g), chopped finely

3cm (1¼-inch) piece fresh ginger (15g), grated

1 clove garlic, crushed

1 teaspoon ground cumin

½ teaspoon each ground coriander, turmeric and garam marsala

¼ teaspoon ground fennel

375g (12 ounces) cauliflower, cut into florets, sliced thickly

350g (11 ounces) butternut pumpkin, cut into 1cm (½-inch) thick slices

1½ cups (375ml) vegetable stock

½ cup (125ml) light coconut milk

½ cup (60g) frozen peas

COCONUT SAMBAL

1 fresh long green chilli, seeded, chopped finely

1 tablespoon coconut flakes

2 tablespoons coarsely chopped fresh coriander (cilantro)

1 Spray a large heated saucepan with oil; cook onion, ginger and garlic, stirring, over high heat, for 3 minutes or until onion softens. Add spices; cook for 1 minute or until fragrant.
2 Stir cauliflower, pumpkin and stock into onion mixture; bring to the boil. Reduce heat; simmer, loosely covered, for 15 minutes or until pumpkin is tender.
3 Add coconut and peas to pan; cook for 2 minutes or until heated through. Season to taste.
4 Make coconut sambal; serve curry sprinkled with coconut sambal.

coconut sambal Combine ingredients in a small bowl.

tips Make a day ahead so the curry flavours can develop overnight. Replace peas with beans, if you like.

89

corn and asparagus fritters

PREP + COOK TIME 15 MINUTES **SERVES** 2

170g (5½ ounces) asparagus

1 cup (160g) frozen corn kernels

1 egg

¼ cup (35g) self-raising flour

1 tablespoon skim milk

2 green onions (scallions), sliced thinly

cooking-oil spray

60g (2 ounces) shaved ham

2 tablespoons reduced-fat cottage cheese

1 Reserve four spears of asparagus; thinly slice remaining asparagus. Bring a medium saucepan of water to the boil, add sliced asparagus and corn; boil for 2 minutes or until heated through. Drain.
2 Whisk egg, flour and milk in a small bowl. Stir in asparagus, corn and onion; season.

3 Lightly spray a heated large non-stick frying pan with oil. Pour two ⅓-cups of the batter into the pan, flatten slightly; cook for 2 minutes or until bubbles appear. Turn fritters; cook until lightly browned on the other side. Transfer to serving plates. Repeat with remaining mixture.
4 Cut reserved asparagus spears diagonally in half. Lightly spray the same pan with oil, add ham and asparagus to heated pan; cook for 2 minutes, turning halfway through cooking time, until lightly golden. Layer fritters with ricotta, ham and asparagus.

tip Replace the asparagus with frozen peas or coarsely grated zucchini.

diary entry

Fritters! This is my favourite breakfast so far this week. I am surprised at how easy it is to make them; they're perfect for a mid-week breakfast treat. – David

nutritional count per serving
▶ 10.1g total fat   ▶ 28.3g carbohydrate
▶ 2.9g saturated fat ▶ 20.5g protein
▶ 1234kJ (295 cal)   ▶ 3.7g fibre

nutritional count per serving
▶ 8.3g total fat
▶ 1.7g saturated fat
▶ 1676kJ (400 cal)
▶ 44.7g carbohydrate
▶ 29.8g protein
▶ 11.5g fibre

mediterranean tuna pasta salad

PREP + COOK TIME 20 MINUTES SERVES 2

cooking-oil spray

200g (6½ ounces) medley tomatoes, quartered

1 large red capsicum (bell pepper) (350g), quartered, seeded

120g (4 ounces) wholemeal spaghetti

100g (3 ounces) green beans, trimmed, cut into 5cm (2-inch) lengths

185g (6 ounces) canned tuna in springwater, drained, flaked coarsely

1 tablespoon red wine vinegar

2 teaspoons olive oil

2 tablespoons baby basil leaves

1 Preheat grill (broiler) to high. Lightly spray two oven trays with oil.

2 Place tomatoes on one tray; place under grill on lower shelf; cook for 10 minutes or until tomatoes start to collapse.

3 Place capsicum on the other tray, skin-side up, place on top shelf of grill; cook for 5 minutes or until skin blackens and blisters. Transfer to a bowl; cover with plastic wrap. Stand for 5 minutes, then peel away skin and slice flesh thinly.

4 Cook pasta in a large saucepan of boiling water until tender. Add beans to pan for last 2 minutes of pasta cooking time; drain. Rinse under cold water; drain.

5 Combine pasta, beans, tomato, capsicum and tuna in a large bowl. Drizzle with vinegar and oil; toss gently to combine, season to taste. Serve salad sprinkled with basil leaves.

tips Put this salad together the night before to take to work. Store in an airtight container in the fridge. Add oil, vinegar and basil just before serving. You can use basil-infused oil olive, if you like. To save time, use 300g (9½ ounces) of well-drained char-grilled capsicum.

test kitchen tips

Add mint leaves and thai basil leaves to the salad for added flavour. To bulk out the salad and increase your vegetable intake you could add 250g (8 ounces) coarsely chopped choy sum with the coriander.

chicken satay skewers with pickled cucumber & carrot salad

PREP + COOK TIME 45 MINUTES (+ STANDING) **SERVES** 2

1 tablespoon finely chopped lemon grass

1 teaspoon ground cumin

½ teaspoon each ground coriander and turmeric

250g (8 ounces) chicken tenderloins, sliced thinly lengthways

⅓ cup (65g) brown rice

1 tablespoon crunchy peanut butter

½ cup (125ml) chicken stock

½ cup loosely packed fresh coriander leaves (cilantro)

PICKLED CUCUMBER & CARROT SALAD

1 large carrot (180g), sliced thinly crossways

1 lebanese cucumber (130g), sliced thinly crossways

2 tablespoons fresh lime juice

2 teaspoons caster (superfine) sugar

1 Make pickled cucumber & carrot salad.

2 Combine lemon grass and spices in a medium bowl; add chicken, toss to coat. Stand mixture for 15 minutes. Thread onto bamboo skewers.

3 Meanwhile, cook rice in a large saucepan of boiling water for 30 minutes or until tender. Drain.

4 Heat a large non-stick frying pan; cook chicken, over medium-high heat, for 2 minutes each side or until golden and cooked through. Remove from pan; cover to keep warm.

5 Reduce heat to low; add peanut butter, stir to combine. Gradually stir in stock; cook, stirring constantly, for 1 minute or until sauce is heated through. Season to taste.

6 Serve chicken on rice, drizzled with sauce. Accompany with salad and top with coriander.

pickled cucumber & carrot salad Combine carrot, cucumber, juice and sugar in a medium bowl; toss gently to combine. Stand for 30 minutes; drain.

tip Soak skewers in water for 30 minutes to prevent them from burning when cooking, or wrap the ends in foil.

nutritional count per serving
▶ 9.9g total fat
▶ 1.9g saturated fat
▶ 1682kJ (402 cal)
▶ 37.8g carbohydrate
▶ 36g protein
▶ 7.7g fibre

savoury french toast

PREP + COOK TIME 10 MINUTES SERVES 2

1 egg

1 tablespoon skim milk

6 slices multigrain french bread stick (90g)

cooking-oil spray

80g (2½ ounces) smoked salmon

½ small avocado (100g), cut into quarters

20g (¾ ounces) rocket leaves (arugula)

1 Whisk egg and milk together in a small bowl; season.

2 Add bread to egg mixture, turn to coat. Stand for 2 minutes or until bread has soaked up the mixture.

3 Lightly spray a large heated non-stick frying pan with oil; add bread to pan, cook, over medium heat, for 2 minutes each side or until golden and cooked through.

4 Place french toast on serving plates; top with salmon, avocado and rocket leaves. Sprinkle with dill, if you like.

tips Serve the french toast topped with shaved ham and roasted cherry tomatoes for a change. Use your favourite bread to toast.

nutritional count per serving

- ▶ 14.8g total fat
- ▶ 3.3g saturated fat
- ▶ 1211kJ (289 cal)
- ▶ 19.5g carbohydrate
- ▶ 17.9g protein
- ▶ 3.3g fibre

chicken, rocket and pear wraps

PREP TIME 30 MINUTES **SERVES** 2

2 wheat mountain bread wraps (50g)

2 tablespoons reduced-fat ricotta

1¼ cups shredded cooked chicken breast (200g)

1 small pear (180g), cored, sliced thinly lengthways

50g (1½ ounce) rocket (arugula) leaves

3 walnut halves, chopped coarsely

1 Spread wraps with ricotta. Top with chicken, pear, rocket and nuts; season. Roll to enclose filling.

tips We used packham pears in this recipe, use your favourite variety. You can poach a chicken breast for this recipe if you like: cover the chicken breast with water and bring to the boil; reduce heat and simmer for 10 minutes. Swap the pear with an apple for a waldorf twist. Replace 1 tablespoon of ricotta and add 2 teaspoons grated parmesan.

diary entry

I must say, I usually associate french toast with fat and sugar, but not so in this case. This savoury version worked a treat for breakfast. Personally I'm not mad about the texture of wraps, I'd rather have bread any day, but the filling was delicious.
– Pamela

nutritional count per serving

▶ 6.5g total fat	▶ 25.8g carbohydrate
▶ 2.1g saturated fat	▶ 36.2g protein
▶ 1308kJ (313 cal)	▶ 3.4g fibre

test kitchen tip

Add toasted fennel seeds for extra fennel flavour.

fennel and sage risotto

PREP + COOK TIME 40 MINUTES **SERVES** 2

2 cups (500ml) vegetable stock

cooking-oil spray

1 small fennel bulb (200g), sliced thinly

1 small brown onion (80g), chopped finely

1 clove garlic, crushed

½ cup (100g) arborio rice

1 cup (85g) coarsely chopped broccoli

1 cup (120g) frozen peas

1 tablespoon finely shredded fresh sage

1 tablespoon finely grated parmesan

1 Bring stock to the boil in a small saucepan. Reduce heat; simmer, covered.

2 Lightly spray a medium saucepan with oil; cook fennel, onion and garlic, stirring, over medium heat, for 5 minutes or until onion softens. Add rice, stir to combine. Stir in ⅓-cup of simmering stock; cook, stirring, over low heat until liquid is absorbed. Continue adding simmering stock in ⅓ cup-batches, stirring until liquid is absorbed after each addition. Total cooking time should be about 20 minutes or until rice is tender.

3 Stir in broccoli and peas; cook, covered, stirring occasionally, for 2 minutes or until tender. Add sage and parmesan; stir to combine. Season to taste.

nutritional count per serving
▶ 4.4g total fat
▶ 1.3g saturated fat
▶ 1296kJ (310 cal)
▶ 50.2g carbohydrate
▶ 12.9g protein
▶ 7.7g fibre

97

fetta, leek and spinach baked eggs

PREP + COOK TIME 25 MINUTES **SERVES** 2

cooking-oil spray

1 small leek (200g), sliced thinly

100g (3 ounces) baby spinach leaves

2 eggs

2 tablespoons skim milk

25g (¾ ounce) reduced-fat fetta, crumbled

2 slices wholegrain bread (90g), toasted

1 Preheat oven to 180°C/350°F. Lightly spray a heated small non-stick frying pan with oil; cook leek, stirring, over medium heat, for 5 minutes or until softened. Add spinach; cook for 2 minutes or until spinach wilts. Season to taste.

2 Divide leek mixture among two ¾-cup (180ml) ovenproof dishes. Crack an egg into each ramekin. Drizzle with milk; sprinkle with fetta. Place on an oven tray; bake for 18 minutes or until the egg is cooked to your liking.

3 Serve toasts with baked eggs.

nutritional count per serving
▶ 9.5g total fat
▶ 3.3g saturated fat
▶ 1044kJ (249 cal)
▶ 20.8g carbohydrate
▶ 17.3g protein
▶ 5.6g fibre

test kitchen tips

The leek can be replaced with thinly sliced green onions; the fetta can be replaced with goat's cheese or crumbled ricotta.

diary entry

The final day of the diet and I had baked eggs for breakfast; what a delicious way for it to end. – David

nutritional count per serving
▶ 3.5g total fat
▶ 0.5g saturated fat
▶ 1593kJ (381 cal)
▶ 56.8g carbohydrate
▶ 23.8g protein
▶ 16.8g fibre

moroccan lentil and kumara salad

PREP + COOK TIME 25 MINUTES **SERVES** 2

1 medium kumara (orange sweet potato) (400g),
cut into 2cm (¾-inch) cubes

½ teaspoon olive oil

1 teaspoon cumin seeds

½ teaspoon each ground cinnamon and coriander

¼ teaspoon ground ginger

¾ cup (150g) french-style lentils

1 small red onion (100g), sliced thinly

40g baby spinach leaves

½ cup coarsely chopped fresh coriander (cilantro)

½ cup coarsely torn fresh mint

1 tablespoon finely grated lemon rind

1 tablespoon lemon juice

1 Preheat oven to 180°C/375°F. Line an oven tray with baking paper. Place kumara on tray, drizzle with oil, sprinkle with seeds and spices; toss to coat kumara in spice mixture. Roast, turning occasionally, for 20 minutes or until kumara is tender.

2 Meanwhile, cook lentils in a saucepan of boiling water for 20 minutes or until tender. Rinse under cold water. Drain.

3 Combine kumara, lentils, onion, spinach, coriander, mint, rind and juice in a large bowl; toss to combine. Season to taste.

tips Replace the kumara with chopped pumpkin, or add ½ cup broad beans (this will add 88kJ/ 21 cal to the serving). Serve the salad warm or cold for lunch at work.

pork, broccolini and cashew stir-fry

PREP + COOK TIME 20 MINUTES **SERVES** 2

50g (1½ ounces) dried rice stick noodles

cooking-oil spray

200g (6½ ounces) pork fillet, sliced thinly

1 medium red onion (170g), cut into wedges

1 clove garlic, sliced thinly

5cm (2-inch) piece fresh ginger (25g),
cut into matchsticks

175g (5½ ounce) broccolini, cut into
5cm (2-inch) lengths

½ teaspoon chinese five-spice powder

¼ cup (60ml) oyster sauce

½ cup fresh thai basil leaves

1 tablespoon toasted cashews, chopped coarsely

1 Place noodles in a large heatproof bowl; cover with boiling water. Stand until just tender; drain.
2 Lightly spray a heated wok with oil; stir-fry pork, in batches, over high heat, for 2 minutes or until browned. Transfer to a small bowl.
3 Add onion, garlic and ginger to wok; stir-fry for 2 minutes. Return pork to wok, add broccolini and spice; stir-fry for 2 minutes or until broccolini is tender. Add sauce; stir-fry until heated through. Remove from heat.
4 Add basil and nuts to wok; toss to combine. Serve with rice noodles.

tips Replace pork with sliced chicken breast or beef rump steak. You can use basil if thai basil is out of season or you could replace the basil with coriander. Broccolini can be swapped with baby corn, if you like. Add a thinly sliced long red chilli to the stir-fry if you'd like extra heat.

diary entry

This diet is about to come to an end. Honestly, there were times I felt the portions were so large I didn't think I could eat it all (I did though). This stir-fry is no different, generous and tasty. – Pamela

nutritional count per serving

▶ 7.7g total fat   ▶ 18.1g carbohydrate
▶ 1.7g saturated fat   ▶ 30.1g protein
▶ 1159kJ (277 cal)   ▶ 6.6g fibre

SNACKS

ALL SNACKS SERVE 2

2x 25g (¾-ounce)
packets pretzels

250g (8 ounces)
strawberries

2 toasted crumpets
drizzled with
1 tablespoon of honey

2 x 200g (6½ ounces)
skim-milk fruit flavoured
yoghurts

2 nectarines

20 rice crackers

4 kiwi fruits

2 plums

250g (8 ounces) punnet
grape tomatoes

1 medium mango (430g),
halved

250g (8 ounces) green
grapes

2 fresh apricots

400g (12½ ounces) rockmelon, cut into wedges

2 small apples

½ avocado sliced over 4 corn thins

250g (8 ounces) cherries

250g (8 ounces) fresh raspberries

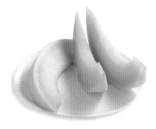

400g (12½ ounces) honeydew melon, cut into wedges

250g (8 ounces) mixed blueberries, strawberries and raspberries

2 medium oranges

2 small pears

400g (12½ ounces) watermelon, cut into wedges

2 small peaches

2 small bananas

yoghurt with pears

PREP TIME 5 MINUTES **SERVES** 2

Combine ½ cup low-fat plain yoghurt and ¼ teaspoon ground cinnamon in a small bowl. Drizzle with ½ teaspoon honey. Serve with 1 cored, thinly sliced medium pear.

tips Use your favourite pear variety or swap the pear for an apple. Use a skim-milk fruit yoghurt, such as passionfruit or strawberry.

nutritional count per serving
- ▶ 0.3g total fat
- ▶ 0.1g saturated fat
- ▶ 438kJ (105 cal)
- ▶ 19.5g carbohydrate
- ▶ 4.5g protein
- ▶ 2.7g fibre

fruit toast with ricotta and banana

PREP TIME 5 MINUTES **SERVES** 2

Toast 2 slices fruit bread (60g). Spread 2 tablespoons of soft reduced-fat ricotta between toast slices. Arrange 1 small sliced banana over ricotta; sprinkle with a pinch of ground cinnamon.

tips Substitute the banana with thinly sliced strawberries. Drizzle with 1 teaspoon of pure maple syrup, if you like.

nutritional count per serving
- ▶ 3g total fat
- ▶ 1.5g saturated fat
- ▶ 633kJ (151 cal)
- ▶ 24.4g carbohydrate
- ▶ 5.4g protein
- ▶ 1.8g fibre

minted pineapple

PREP TIME 5 MINUTES **SERVES** 2

Peel and chop 200g (6½ ounces) pineapple. Combine pineapple with 1 tablespoon baby mint leaves in a medium bowl.

tip Swap the pineapple for watermelon, if you like.

vanilla strawberries and watermelon

PREP TIME 10 MINUTES **SERVES** 2

Cut 200g (6½ ounces) watermelon into 2cm (¾-inch) wedges. Combine watermelon with 250g (8 ounces) halved strawberries and ½ teaspoon vanilla extract in a small bowl.

tip Add shredded mint leaves or sprinkle with ground cinnamon for extra flavour.

---

nutritional count per serving

▶ 0.7g total fat	▶ 4.2g carbohydrate
▶ 0g saturated fat	▶ 0.6g protein
▶ 95kJ (22 cal)	▶ 1.2g fibre

nutritional count per serving

▶ 0.3g total fat	▶ 8.4g carbohydrate
▶ 0g saturated fat	▶ 2.4g protein
▶ 222kJ (53 cal)	▶ 3.3g fibre

radish with green onion cottage cheese

PREP TIME 5 MINUTES **SERVES** 2

Cut 4 radishes into quarters. Combine ⅓ cup reduced-fat cottage cheese, 1 crushed garlic clove and 1 thinly sliced green onion; serve with radish.

celery with chilli cream cheese

PREP TIME 5 MINUTES **SERVES** 2

Combine 2 tablespoons each of reduced-fat cream cheese and finely chopped fresh chives, and half a finely chopped red thai (serrano) chilli in a small bowl; season to taste. Serve with 2 trimmed celery sticks, cut into 10cm (4-inch) lengths.

tips Replace chives with chopped coriander and add a little lime juice for an Asian twist. Remove seeds from the chilli, if you don't like the heat.

nutritional count per serving

▶ 6.2g total fat   ▶ 2.9g carbohydrate
▶ 4.2g saturated fat   ▶ 8g protein
▶ 435kJ (104 cal)   ▶ 0.7g fibre

nutritional count per serving

▶ 3.4g total fat   ▶ 1.9g carbohydrate
▶ 2.2g saturated fat   ▶ 2.4g protein
▶ 216kJ (52 cal)   ▶ 2.1g fibre

edamame with sumac

PREP + COOK TIME 5 MINUTES **SERVES** 2

Cook 200g (6½ ounces) frozen edamame peas in pods in a large saucepan of boiling water for 2 minutes or until heated through. Drain. Transfer to a bowl and sprinkle with ½ teaspoon each of sea salt flakes and sumac; toss to combine. Serve peas immediately.

tip Edamame are fresh green baby soya beans, they are available from major supermarkets and Asian grocery stores; they are also available frozen. Edamame may be cooked in the microwave; follow the directions on the packet.

nutritional count per serving
▶ 2g total fat ▶ 5.8g carbohydrate
▶ 0.3g saturated fat ▶ 4.8g protein
▶ 275kJ (66 cal) ▶ 1.8g fibre

carrot sticks with cream cheese

PREP TIME 5 MINUTES **SERVES** 2

Cut 2 small carrots into sticks; serve with ⅓ cup reduced-fat spreadable cream cheese.

nutritional count per serving
▶ 6.7g total fat ▶ 4.2g carbohydrate
▶ 4.4g saturated fat ▶ 3.8g protein
▶ 399kJ (95 cal) ▶ 1.7g fibre

boiled eggs
with dukkah salt

PREP + COOK TIME 10 MINUTES **SERVES** 2

Place 2 eggs in a small saucepan and cover with cold water. Bring to the boil; boil, uncovered, for 3½ minutes, drain. When cool enough to handle, shell eggs. To serve, sprinkle eggs with 2 teaspoons almond dukkah.

tips Serve boiled eggs sprinkled with chive or lemon salt as an alternative to dukkah. Dukkah is an Egyptian spice blend made of roasted nuts and aromatic spices. It is available from Middle-Eastern food stores, specialty spice stores and most major supermarkets.

trail mix

PREP TIME 5 MINUTES **SERVES** 2

Combine ½ cup puffed rice, 5 halved almonds, 2 halved walnuts, 2 teaspoons pepitas (dried pumpkin seeds), 4 chopped dates and a pinch of cinnamon in a small bowl; toss to combine.

tip Replace the walnuts or almonds with hazelnuts or cashews.

nutritional count per serving
- ▶ 7.5g total fat
- ▶ 1.9g saturated fat
- ▶ 421kJ (101 cal)
- ▶ 0.4g carbohydrate
- ▶ 7.7g protein
- ▶ 0g fibre

nutritional count per serving
- ▶ 5.1g total fat
- ▶ 0.5g saturated fat
- ▶ 434kJ (104 cal)
- ▶ 11.5g carbohydrate
- ▶ 2.3g protein
- ▶ 1.5g fibre

popcorn with cajun spice

PREP TIME 5 MINUTES **SERVES** 2

Combine 40g (1½ ounces) air-popped popcorn and ¼ teaspoon cajun seasoning in a medium bowl; toss until well coated.

tip You can buy pre-cooked air-popped popcorn from supermarkets.

pappadums with cucumber raita

PREP TIME 5 MINUTES **SERVES** 2

Combine 2 tablespoons skim-milk yoghurt and half a finely chopped lebanese cucumber in a small bowl; season to taste. Serve with 25g (¾-ounce) mini pappadums.

tip Add chopped mint for a fresh Indian flavour.

nutritional count per serving
- ▶ 0.9g total fat
- ▶ 0.1g saturated fat
- ▶ 292kJ (70 cal)
- ▶ 11.1g carbohydrate
- ▶ 2.6g protein
- ▶ 3g fibre

nutritional count per serving
- ▶ 4.6g total fat
- ▶ 0.2g saturated fat
- ▶ 239kJ (57 cal)
- ▶ 7.1g carbohydrate
- ▶ 4.6g protein
- ▶ 2.7g fibre

berry smoothie

PREP TIME 5 MINUTES **SERVES** 2

Blend 2 cups skim milk with 150g (4½ ounces) frozen mixed berries until smooth.

green smoothie

PREP TIME 10 MINUTES **SERVES** 2

Blend or process 1 peeled coarsely chopped lime, 1 peeled, cored, coarsely chopped medium apple, 1 peeled coarsely chopped lebanese cucumber, 320ml (10 ounces) canned coconut water, 30g (1 ounce) baby spinach leaves and 5g (¼ ounce) finely grated ginger until smooth.

tip Use a variety of green vegetables or fruits, such as lettuce, pear or honeydew melon.

nutritional count per serving

▶ 0.4g total fat   ▶ 17.7g carbohydrate
▶ 0.3g saturated fat   ▶ 10.3g protein
▶ 507kJ (121 cal)   ▶ 2.9g fibre

nutritional count per serving

▶ 0.4g total fat   ▶ 16.2g carbohydrate
▶ 0.2g saturated fat   ▶ 1.9g protein
▶ 349kJ (83 cal)   ▶ 3.2g fibre

corn cakes with tomato & basil salsa

PREP TIME 5 MINUTES **SERVES** 2

Combine 80g (2½ ounces) coarsely chopped mixed medley tomatoes and 2 tablespoons finely shredded fresh basil in a small bowl; season to taste. Spoon onto 2 corn cakes to serve.

tip Replace basil with parsley leaves or shredded mint leaves.

nutritional count per serving
- ▶ 0.4g total fat
- ▶ 0.1g saturated fat
- ▶ 180kJ (43 cal)
- ▶ 8g carbohydrate
- ▶ 1.1g protein
- ▶ 1.3g fibre

cottage cheese and cucumber crackers

PREP TIME 5 MINUTES **SERVES** 2

Spread 4 rice and corn squares with 1 tablespoon low-fat cottage cheese; top with 1 thinly sliced cucumber, season to taste.

nutritional count per serving
- ▶ 1.3g total fat
- ▶ 0.5g saturated fat
- ▶ 390kJ (93 cal)
- ▶ 15.8g carbohydrate
- ▶ 3.4g protein
- ▶ 2g fibre

PANTRY STAPLES

OIL

- cooking-oil spray
- 1 small bottle olive oil
- 1 bottle sesame oil
- 1 small bottle vegetable oil

STOCK

- 500ml beef consommé or stock
- 625ml chicken stock
- 1 x 500ml salt-reduced chicken stock
- 1 packet salt-reduced chicken stock powder
- 1 litre vegetable stock

SPICES

- cajun seasoning
- cardamom pods
- chilli flakes
- chinese five-spice
- cloves, whole
- fennel seeds
- ground fennel
- garam masala
- ground cinnamon
- cinnamon sticks
- ground coriander
- ground cumin
- cumin seeds
- ground ginger
- ground turmeric
- mixed spice
- smoked paprika
- sweet paprika
- cracked black pepper
- sea salt flakes
- sesame seeds
- star anise
- sumac
- za'atar

SPREADS

- 1 jar honey
- 1 bottle maple syrup
- 1 small jar crunchy peanut butter

SAUCES & DRESSINGS

- 1 jar dijon mustard
- 1 bottle low-fat dijonnaise
- 1 jar wholegrain mustard
- 1 bottle 99% fat-free french dressing
- 1 small jar 99%-free mayonnaise
- 1 small bottle hot chilli sauce
- 1 small bottle balsamic vinegar
- 1 small bottle red wine vinegar
- 1 bottle rice wine vinegar
- 1 small bottle white wine vinegar
- 1 bottle light soy sauce
- 1 bottle tamari
- 1 bottle fish sauce
- 1 small jar harissa paste
- 1 small bottle plum sauce
- 1 bottle oyster sauce
- 1 small bottle sweet chilli sauce
- 1 small bottle worcestershire sauce
- 1 tube wasabi

DRIED FRUIT & NUTS

- 1 small packet almonds
- 1 packet ground almonds
- 1 packet toasted slivered almonds
- 1 tablespoon cashews
- 1 packet dried cranberries
- 1 packet currants
- 1 packet seedless dates
- 1 packet dried figs
- 1 packet pepitas (pumpkin seeds)
- 1 small packet pistachio nuts
- 1 small packet raisins
- 1 small packet walnuts

PASTA, RICE & NOODLES

- 1 packet wholemeal penne
- 1 packet soba noodles
- 1 packet rice paper rounds
- 1 packet rice stick noodles
- 150g rice vermicelli
- 1 small packet arborio rice
- 1 small packet brown rice
- 1 x 250g packaged 90-second brown rice

FLOUR

- 1 packet plain flour
- 1 packet wholemeal plain flour
- 1 packet self-raising flour
- 1 packet wholemeal self-raising flour
- 1 packet buckwheat flour

BAKING ESSENTIALS

- 1 packet baking powder
- 1 small packet bicarbonate
- of soda
- 1 small bottle vanilla extract
- 1 jar vanilla bean paste
- 1 bottle rosewater
- 1 packet caster sugar
- 1 small packet brown sugar

CEREALS

- 1 small packet coconut flakes
- 1 packet air-popped popcorn
- 1 small packet puffed rice
- 1 packet quinoa flakes
- 1 packet red quinoa
- 1 packet rolled rye
- 1 packet rolled oats
- 1 packet wheat bran flakes
- 1 small packet wholemeal couscous

CANNED VEGETABLES

- 1 small can sliced beetroot
- 2 x 400g cans cannellini beans
- 1 jar char-grilled capsicum
- 420g can chickpeas
- 11 x 400g cans diced tomatoes
- 1 small can kidney beans
- 1 small jar pickled cucumber

CONDIMENTS & PASTES

- 1 small bottle dark agave syrup
- 1 small jar basil pesto
- 1 small jar mango chutney
- 1 small jar tandoori paste

BREAD

- 1 packet dry breadcrumbs
- 1 packet corn thins
- 1 packet crumpets
- 1 small wholemeal french stick
- 1 loaf fruit bread
- 1 packet multigrain english muffins
- 1 loaf multigrain bread
- 25g mini papadums
- 2 x 25g packet pretzels
- 1 packet roti bread
- 1 packet rice crackers
- 1 loaf dark rye bread
- 1 loaf sourdough bread
- 1 loaf soy and quinoa bread

- 1 packet wholegrain tortillas
- 1 packet white corn tortillas
- 1 packet wholemeal bread
- 1 loaf wholegrain bread
- 1 packet wheat mountain bread wraps
- 1 packet wholegrain soft wraps
- 1 packet wholemeal pocket pitta bread

MISCELLANEOUS

- 1 packet almond dukkah
- 1 jar baby salted capers
- 1 small can light coconut milk
- 320ml can coconut water
- 1 small jar preserved lemons
- 1 packet pickled ginger
- 1 small packet french-style green lentils
- 1 small jar pickled jalapeño chillies
- 1 packet nori seaweed
- 1 small jar pimento-stuffed olives
- 1 small jar pomegranate molasses
- 1 jar spicy tomato salsa
- 2 x 185g cans tuna in springwater
- 1 can sliced canned water chestnuts

GLOSSARY

BACON, SHORTCUT is a 'half rasher'; the streaky (belly), narrow portion of the rasher has been removed leaving the choice cut eye meat (fat end).

BAKING POWDER a raising agent consisting mainly of two parts cream of tartar to one part bicarbonate of soda (baking soda), which, when combined, lightens the mixture during baking.

BEANS
broad also known as fava, windsor and horse beans; peel fresh and frozen beans twice (discarding the outer long green pod and the beige-green tough inner shell).
cannellini a small white bean similar in appearance and flavour to other white beans (great northern, navy or haricot). Available dried or canned.
edamame green baby soya beans; available fresh and frozen from major supermarkets and Asian grocery stores.
green also known as french or string beans (although the tough string they once had has generally been bred out of them); this long thin fresh bean is consumed in its entirety once cooked.
kidney medium-sized red or white bean, slightly floury in texture yet sweet in flavour; sold dried or canned.
sprouts also known as bean shoots; tender new growths of assorted beans and seeds.

BEEF
eye fillet a very tender cut from the area below the rib cage; also known as beef tenderloin.
minute steaks a thinly sliced cut of beef so it cooks quickly. Can be blade, oyster, round or just about any other cut.

BICARBONATE OF SODA also known as baking or carb soda; used as a raising agent in baking.

BLOOD ORANGE a virtually seedless citrus fruit with blood-red rind and flesh; it has a sweet, non-acidic pulp and juice.

BRAN FLAKES made from the outer layer of a cereal, most often the husks of wheat, rice or oats, which is flattened into light, dry flakes.

BREAD
english muffin a round teacake made from yeast, flour, milk, some semolina and salt; often confused with crumpets. Sold in most supermarkets; split open and toast before eating.
french stick dough that's been formed into a long, narrow cylindrical loaf. It has a crisp brown crust and light chewy interior. It is also known as french bread, french loaf or baguette.
mountain wraps a soft-textured, thin, flat bread used for sandwiches, or filled and rolled up.
pitta also known as lebanese bread; a wheat-flour pocket bread sold in large, flat pieces that separate into two thin rounds. Also available in small thick pieces called pocket pitta.
sourdough has a lightly sour taste from the yeast-starter culture used to make the bread. A low-risen bread with a dense centre and crisp crust.
tortillas thin, round unleavened bread originating in Mexico. Two kinds are available, one made from wheat flour and the other from corn (maize meal).

BUTTERMILK originally the term given to the slightly sour liquid left after butter was churned from cream, today it is made similarly to yoghurt. Sold alongside fresh milk products in supermarkets; despite the implication of its name, it's low in fat.

BUTTERNUT PUMPKIN (squash) a member of the gourd family. Butternut is pear-shaped with golden skin and orange flesh.

CAPSICUM also known as bell pepper or, simply, pepper. Membranes and seeds should be discarded before use.

CHEESE
cottage cheese fresh, white, unripened curd cheese with a grainy consistency and a fat content between 5% and 15%.
light cream cheese commonly known as Philadelphia or Philly, a soft cows-milk cheese available as a blend of cottage and cream cheeses with a fat content of 21%.
parmesan also known as parmigiano, a hard, grainy cows-milk cheese. The curd is salted in brine for a month before being aged for up to two years.

CHICKEN
breast fillet is skinned and boned.
smoked ready-to-eat, available as a whole small bird or breasts; sold cryovac-packed in supermarkets.
tenderloin the small strip of meat under the breast.

CHILLI, JALAPEÑO a fairly hot green chilli; available bottled in brine or fresh from specialty greengrocers.

CINNAMON dried inner bark of the shoots of the cinnamon tree; available in stick (quill) or ground form.

CORIANDER also known as pak chee, cilantro or chinese parsley; bright-green leafy herb with a pungent flavour. Both the stems and roots of coriander are used in cooking; wash well before using. Is also available ground or as seeds; don't substitute these for fresh coriander as the tastes are completely different.

CORNFLOUR (cornstarch) used as a thickening agent. Available as wheaten and 100% maize (corn) cornflour.

COUSCOUS a fine, grain-like cereal product made from semolina; a dough of semolina flour and water is sieved then dehydrated to produce minuscule even-sized pellets of couscous. It is rehydrated by steaming, or with the addition of a warm liquid, and swells to three or four times its original size.

CUMIN, GROUND a spice also known as zeera or comino, resembling caraway in size; has a spicy, nutty flavour. Also available dried (ground).

DIJONNAISE a blend of dijon mustard and mayonnaise.

EGGS some recipes in this book may call for raw or barely cooked eggs; exercise caution if there is a salmonella problem in your area. The risk is greater for those who are pregnant, elderly or very young, and those with impaired immune systems.

ENGLISH MUFFIN see bread.

FILLO PASTRY (also filo and phyllo); tissue-thin pastry sheets.

FISH
firm white fillets blue eye, bream, flathead, swordfish, ling, whiting, jewfish, snapper or sea perch are all good choices. Check for any small pieces of bone in the fillets and use tweezers to remove them.
salmon has a red-pink firm flesh with few bones, and a moist delicate flavour.
trout a delicately flavoured soft, pink-fleshed fish belonging to the same family as salmon (which can be substituted).

FLOUR
buckwheat is a herb belonging to the same plant family as rhubarb; it is not a cereal, so is gluten-free. It is available as a flour; ground into coarse, medium or fine grain.

plain a general all-purpose flour made from wheat; has no added baking powder.

self-raising (rising) plain or wholemeal flour sifted with baking powder in the proportion of 1 cup plain (all-purpose) flour to 2 teaspoons baking powder.

wholemeal plain a general all-purpose wholewheat flour milled from whole wheat grain (bran, germ and endosperm).

GARAM MASALA a blend of spices based on cardamom, cinnamon, cloves, coriander, fennel and cumin, roasted and ground together. Black pepper and chilli can be added for a hotter version.

GINGER, **FRESH** also known as green or root ginger; is the thick root of a tropical plant. Trim, removing any creases and knobbly pieces, then grate or slice thinly.

pickled paper-thin shavings of ginger are pickled in a mixture of vinegar, sugar and natural colouring. Available from Asian food shops.

GOLDEN SYRUP a by-product of refined sugar cane; pure maple syrup or honey can be substituted.

HARISSA a Moroccan sauce or paste made from dried chillies, cumin, garlic, oil and caraway seeds. The paste, available in a tube, is very hot and should not be used in large amounts; bottled harissa sauce is more mild, but if you're not used to heat, even this may be too hot. From supermarkets and Middle-Eastern grocery stores.

LAMB

backstrap the larger fillet from a row of loin chops or cutlets. Lamb fillet may be substituted, although this cut is a little smaller than the backstrap.

cutlets small, tender rib chop.

LENTILS, FRENCH-STYLE GREEN related to the famous french lentils du puy; dark green-blue, tiny lentils with a nutty, earthy flavour and a hardy nature that allows them to be rapidly cooked without disintegrating. Are also known as australian, bondi or matilda lentils.

LETTUCE

butter have small, round, loosely formed heads with soft, buttery-textured leaves ranging from pale green on the outer leaves to pale yellow-green on the inner leaves. Has a sweet flavour.

cos also known as romaine lettuce.

iceberg a heavy, firm round lettuce with tightly packed crisp leaves.

KIPFLER POTATOES (fingerling) small, finger-shaped potatoes with a nutty flavour; great baked and in salads.

MAPLE SYRUP, PURE a thin syrup distilled from the sap of the maple tree. Maple-flavoured syrup or pancake syrup is not an adequate substitute.

MUSTARD

dijon pale brown, distinctively flavoured, fairly mild tasting french mustard.

wholegrain is also known as seeded mustard. A french-style coarse-grain mustard made from crushed mustard seeds and dijon-style french mustard.

OIL

cooking spray we use a cholesterol-free spray made from canola oil.

olive made from ripened olives. Extra virgin and virgin are the best, while extra light or light refers to taste, not fat levels.

peanut pressed from ground peanuts; is the most commonly used oil in Asian cooking because of its high smoke point (can handle high heat without burning).

sesame made from roasted, crushed, white sesame seeds.

vegetable sourced from plants.

ONION

brown and white are interchangeable, however, white onions have a more pungent flesh.

green an immature onion picked before the bulb has formed, having a long, bright-green edible stalk. Also known as scallion or, incorrectly, shallot.

red also known as spanish, red spanish or bermuda onion; sweet-flavoured, large, purple-red onion.

spring have small white bulbs and long narrow green-leafed tops.

PAPRIKA ground, dried red capsicum (bell pepper); there are many grades and types available, including sweet, hot, mild and smoked.

PASTRAMI the word derives from the Romanian word 'pastra', which means 'to preserve'. Highly seasoned preserved meat usually made from beef.

PEPITAS dried pumpkin seeds.

PORK

fillets (tenderloin) comes from the full pork loin. As the name indicates, the tenderloin is one of the most tender cuts of pork.

steaks, boneless from the loin, which runs along most of the back.

tenderloin see fillet.

PRESERVED LEMON RIND a North African specialty; lemons are quartered and preserved in salt and lemon juice or water. To use, remove and discard pulp, squeeze juice from rind, rinse rind well; slice thinly. Sold in jars or singly by most delicatessens; once opened, store under refrigeration.

RED RADISH peppery root vegetable related to the mustard plant. The small round red variety is the mildest; it is crisp and juicy, and eaten raw in salads.

RHUBARB has thick, celery-like stalks that can reach up to 60cm long (choose fresh crisp stalks); the stalks are the only edible portion of the plant – the leaves contain a toxic substance. Although rhubarb is generally eaten as a fruit, it is a vegetable.

RICE

arborio originated from the town of Arborio in Italy. A small, round-grained rice suited to absorb a large amount of liquid; when cooked, the grain becomes firm, creamy and chewy in texture.

brown retains the outer bran layer of the rice grain. When cooked, it has a slightly chewy texture and a delicate nut-like flavour.

ROLLED OATS oat groats (which are oats that have been husked) that have been steamed-softened, flattened with rollers, dried and then packaged for consumption as a cereal product.

SAUCE

fish called naam pla on the label if it is Thai made; the Vietnamese version, nuoc naam, is almost identical. Made from pulverised salted fermented fish (most often anchovies); has a pungent smell and a strong taste. There are many versions of varying intensity, so use according to your taste.

oyster Asian in origin, this rich, brown sauce is made from oysters and their brine, cooked with salt and soy sauce, and thickened with starches.

plum a thick, sweet and sour sauce made from plums, vinegar, sugar, chillies and spices.

soy made from fermented soya beans. Several variations are available in most supermarkets and Asian food stores. We use a mild Japanese-style variety in our recipes; possibly the best table soy and the one to choose if you only want to use one variety.

light soy fairly thin in consistency and, while paler than the others, is the saltiest tasting; used in dishes in which the natural colour of the ingredients is to be maintained. Not to be confused with salt-reduced or low-sodium soy sauces.

sweet chilli a mild, Thai-style sauce made from red chillies, sugar, garlic and vinegar.

tamari similar to, but thicker than, japanese soy sauce; very dark in colour with a distinctively mellow flavour.

tomato also known as ketchup or catsup; a flavoured condiment made from tomatoes, vinegar and spices.

worcestershire this dark brown spicy condiment is made from soy sauce, garlic, tamarind, onions, molasses, lime, anchovies, vinegar and other seasonings. It is available in most supermarkets.

SCALLOPS a bivalve mollusc with a fluted shell valve; we use scallops that have the coral (roe) removed. Available on the half-shell or shelled.

SKIM MILK has less than or equal to 0.15 per cent fat. Sometimes milk solids are added to optimise the taste.

SNOW PEAS also mange tout ('eat all'). *Snow pea tendrils*, the growing shoots of the plant, are sold by greengrocers. *Snow pea sprouts* are the tender new growths of snow peas, and are also known as mange tout.

SUGAR
brown a finely granulated, extremely soft sugar retaining molasses for its characteristic colour and flavour.

caster also known as superfine or finely granulated table sugar.

palm also known as nam tan pip, jawa, jaggery or gula melaka; made from the sap of the sugar palm tree. Light brown to black in colour and usually sold in rock-hard cakes. If palm sugar is unavailable, substitute with brown sugar, instead.

white a coarse, granulated table sugar, also known as crystal sugar.

SULTANAS dried grapes, also known as golden raisins.

SUMAC a purple-red, astringent spice ground from berries growing on wild shrubs around the Mediterranean; has a tart, lemony flavour.

SUNFLOWER KERNELS dried husked sunflower seeds.

TACO SEASONING MIX a packaged seasoning meant to duplicate the mexican sauce made from oregano, cumin, chillies and other spices.

TAMARI see sauces.

TANDOORI CURRY PASTE a mild blend of paprika, lemon juice, garlic, onion and various spices combined with yoghurt and used as a marinade.

TERIYAKI MARINADE a blend of soy sauce, wine, vinegar and spices.

TIKKA MASALA CURRY PASTE is a mild aromatic, slightly smoky, rich curry based on tomatoes and cream or coconut cream.

TOFU also known as bean curd, an off-white, custard-like product made from the 'milk' of crushed soya beans; comes fresh as soft or firm. Leftover fresh tofu can be refrigerated in water (which is changed daily) up to four days.

TOMATO
cherry also known as tiny tim or tom thumb tomatoes, small and round.

grape are about the size of a grape; they can be oblong, pear or grape-shaped and are often used whole in salads or eaten as a snack.

paste triple-concentrated tomato puree that's used to flavour soups, stews, sauces and casseroles.

roma also called egg or plum; these are the smallish, oval-shaped tomatoes much used in Italian cooking.

semi-dried partially dried tomato pieces in olive oil; softer and juicier than sun-dried, these are not a preserve so do not keep as long as sun-dried tomatoes.

sun-dried we use sun-dried tomatoes packaged in oil, unless otherwise specified; drain well before using.

tomato medley contains a mix of red and yellow grape tomatoes, baby roma (egg) tomatoes, dark green/brown zebrino tomatoes and red and yellow cherry tomatoes. Each tomato has a distinct shape, size or flavour.

VANILLA EXTRACT made by pulping chopped vanilla beans with a mixture of alcohol and water. This gives a very strong solution, and only a couple of drops are needed to flavour most dishes.

VIETNAMESE MINT not a mint at all, but a narrow-leafed, pungent herb; also known as cambodian mint and laksa leaf (daun laksa), is widely used in many Asian soups and salads.

VINEGAR
balsamic made from the juice of trebbiano grapes; it is a deep rich brown colour with a sweet and sour flavour. Originally from Modena, Italy, there are now many balsamic vinegars on the market ranging in pungency and quality, depending on how long they have been aged. Quality can be determined up to a point by price; use the most expensive sparingly.

brown malt made from fermented malt and beech shavings.

cider (apple cider) made from crushed fermented apples.

red wine based on a blend of fermented red wine.

rice a colourless vinegar made from fermented rice and flavoured with sugar and salt. Also known as seasoned rice vinegar.

white wine made from a blend of white wines.

WASABI (japanese horseradish) is available as a paste in tubes or powdered in tins from Asian food stores and some supermarkets. Used to make the pungent, green-coloured sauce traditionally served with Japanese raw fish dishes.

WATER CHESTNUTS resembles a chestnut in appearance, hence the English name. Are small brown tubers with a crisp, white, nutty-tasting flesh. Canned water chestnuts are more easily obtained and can be kept about a month, once opened, under refrigeration.

WATERCRESS also known as winter rocket, is a slightly peppery, dark-green leaf vegetable commercially cultivated and also found growing in the wild. Highly perishable, so must be used as soon as possible after purchase.

WEET-BIX oven-roasted whole wheat grains and barley malt extract – it is a wheat-based breakfast biscuit.

WOMBOK also known as petsai or peking, chinese or napa cabbage. Elongated in shape with pale green, crinkly leaves.

YOGHURT, LOW-FAT we used yoghurt with a fat content of less than 0.2%.

ZA'ATAR a blend of whole roasted sesame seeds, sumac and crushed dried herbs such as wild marjoram and thyme; its content is largely determined by the individual maker. Available in delicatessens and specialty food stores.

INDEX

Published in 2014 by Bauer Media Books

Bauer Media Books is a division of Bauer Media Limited

54 Park St, Sydney

GPO Box 4088, Sydney, NSW 2001.

phone (02) 9282 8618; fax (02) 9126 3702

www.awwcookbooks.com.au

MEDIA GROUP

BAUER MEDIA BOOKS

Publisher - Sally Wright

Editorial and Food Director - Pamela Clark

Sales & Rights Director Brian Cearnes

Creative Director - Hieu Chi Nguyen

Published and Distributed in the United Kingdom by Octopus Publishing Group

Endeavour House

189 Shaftesbury Avenue

London WC2H 8JY

United Kingdom

phone (+44)(0)207 632 5400; fax (+44)(0)207 632 5405

info@octopus-publishing.co.uk;

www.octopusbooks.co.uk

Printed by Toppan Printing Co., China

International foreign language rights, Brian Cearnes, Bauer Media Books bcearnes@bauer-media.com.au

A catalogue record for this book is available from the British Library.

ISBN: 978-174245-428-3 (paperback)

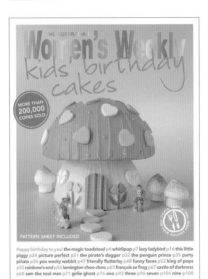
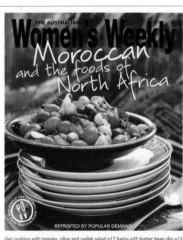